CW0055145O

SELL *Yourself* TO

SCIENCE

The Complete Guide to Selling Your Organs, Body Fluids, Bodily Functions and Being a Human Guinea Pig

by Jim Hogshire

Loompanics Unlimited
Port Townsend, Washington

For Jumpy

This book is sold for information purposes only. Neither the author nor the publisher will be held accountable for the use or misuse of the information contained in this book

SELL YOURSELF TO SCIENCE
The Complete Guide to Selling Your Organs, Body Fluids, Bodily Functions, and Being a Human Guinea Pig

Published by:
Loompanics Unlimited
PO Box 1197
Port Townsend, WA 98364
Loompanics Unlimited is a division of Loompanics Enterprises, Inc.

Cover and interior illustrations by Mark Zingarelli
Anatomical chart by Daniel Wend/MEDIA Graphics

ISBN 1-55950-084-0
Library of Congress Catalog Card Number 92-081803

SELL *Yourself* TO *SCIENCE*

has been written about in *Harper's, Hustler, USA Today, The L.A.Reader, The Nose, The Village Voice,* and many other papers, magazines and book reviews. Here's what they're saying about this "incredible-but-true" book:

"You might view this tome as pretty off-center, but it's well thought out and includes much practical information."
    — **Booklist (The American Library Association)**

"This book is three things: 1) an honest-to-goodness (and-detailed) prescription for making a living off your body; 2) an unbridled call for legalizing organ sales; 3) a parody of the how-to genre of books."
    — **NUVO**

"Always entertaining, *Sell Yourself* encourages entrepreneurship, time and again proving punk band Gang of Four's edict that "the body is good business."
    — **VLS (The Village Voice Literary Supplement)**

"You can make money off your body products while you're still alive and kicking. Here's how."
    — **National Examiner**

"Before you make another trip to the emergency room, order *Sell Yourself to Science*... Mouth loves this book."
    — **The Mouth**

"Organ donation can be a profitable business. Give the gift of organs this holiday season."
    — **Hustler**

"*Sell Yourself to Science* is an eye-opening and sometimes mind-bending read.... The definitive how-to for the human guinea-pig and body-part business."
    — **Welcomat Book Review**

Contents

Part Two — Piece by Piece

Appendixes

How Much Are You Worth?

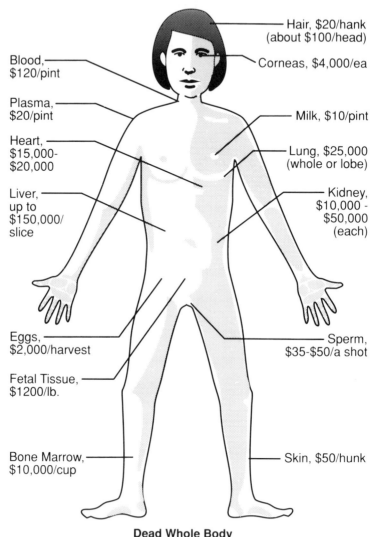

Hair, $20/hank (about $100/head)

Corneas, $4,000/ea

Blood, $120/pint

Plasma, $20/pint

Heart, $15,000-$20,000

Liver, up to $150,000/slice

Milk, $10/pint

Lung, $25,000 (whole or lobe)

Kidney, $10,000 - $50,000 (each)

Eggs, $2,000/harvest

Fetal Tissue, $1200/lb.

Sperm, $35-$50/a shot

Bone Marrow, $10,000/cup

Skin, $50/hunk

Dead Whole Body
$50,000 if dead less than 15 hours
$1,000 if dead more than 15 hours

Alive Whole Body
Guinea Pigging: $100 per day plus room & board
Working: $4.25 per hour, minimum wage

Introduction

THERE USED TO BE an old saw that the human body was worth only 95 cents when reduced to its basic chemistry. Maybe this thought was supposed to humble us and make us appreciate the grandeur that is life. In any case, it needs a little updating.

Today, a kidney alone is worth up to $50,000. That should make us appreciate the grandeur of modern medicine. Our body parts have become so valuable that we might start seeing ourselves as human cash machines: containers made of flesh and bone, storing precious organs in a climate-controlled environment. This book is about how to make a withdrawal.

The value of the human body creates many difficult social problems and moral dilemmas. While graverobbing has a long tradition, it is being practiced today on an unprecedented scale. There have been stories of people killed for their corneas, worth about $4,000 on the current world market. In early 1992, there was a legal battle over the organs of a Florida baby born without a brain. For a society uncomfortable with death, you can imagine the discomfort caused by parting-out the dead and dying.

These problems are best illustrated by a simple fact: each year, thousands of people die for lack of a kidney transplant while millions of people take perfectly good kidneys to the grave with them. There is a solution to this problem: allow people to sell their organs.

It seems ridiculous that people own cars, houses, furniture and clothes, but they don't own themselves. If they did, their bodies would become part of their estate when they die, and could be sold off, in whole or in part, for the benefit of their heirs. No one would be condemned to spend the rest of their life stuck on a dialysis machine at a cost of $25,000 a year. And many others would benefit from corneas, bone marrow, tissue, organs and other body parts that are now either incinerated or thrown in the ground to rot because potential donors have no incentive to sell.

In fact, everybody *but* the donor is allowed to profit from organ transplants. When an organ donor dies, he or she sets into motion more than $1 million worth of medical procedures. The organ banks get paid, the hospitals get paid, the doctors and their assistants all collect their fees. The organ recipient benefits more than anyone, perhaps with a new lease on life. But it is against the law to give money to the donor, so most potential donors keep their organs to themselves. Perhaps this book will change all that.

PART ONE of this book deals with how you can legally profit by renting out your body for experimentation. Being a professional test subject, or "human guinea pig," is one of the easiest and most rewarding ways to make a living off your body. You can earn up to $100 a day, plus benefits, helping pharmaceutical companies test drugs. Though not always pleasant, the work is safe, requires no skill, and has the side benefit of helping bring comfort to the ill.

In this section, you'll learn what it's like being a human guinea pig. We'll quiz people who make a living as guinea pigs about working conditions. The reader will learn how drugs become legal, how they are tested, and what sorts of tests are most common. There's also practical information on how to find testing programs, including a list of over 150 active test sites in the U.S.A.

PART TWO deals with actually selling your body parts or products. Some of this is legal in the United States, some of it's not. But all of it is legal somewhere in the world. And current court battles make me suspect that organ selling will be legalized in the U.S., hopefully before it comes my turn to cash in.

In this section, I give the current world market prices for most of your bodily goods. Of course, prices are subject to change without notice. You'll also learn why everything is worth as much as it is, and what factors affect pricing.

Lots of body parts and products can be sold while you're alive: bone marrow, blood, sperm, hair, etc. Others, like your heart and brain, are best not sold until you don't need your body anymore. I'll explain how some folks will try anything to get you to give away your body parts or those of a loved one, and how you can hold out for some compensation, even in the United States.

THERE IS NOTHING IMMORAL about renting or selling your body. The idea that there is something wrong with this is rooted in the same tradition as the fantasy that "if you work hard enough someday the boss will notice you and promote you." In other words, it serves the purposes of those folks who have no problem with breaking your back all your life then, when you are dead, mining your corpse for life-saving organs. On the contrary, one can make a very good case that *refusing* to allow people to sell the most personal of all property is immoral, resulting in the waste of valuable resources and the loss of life.

This book rests on the idea that your body, including anything it produces, belongs to you and you alone. It was given to you by God to do with what you will, for whatever purpose you choose. The fact that you can do a lot of good for yourself and for others by renting and selling your body only reaffirms this truth. One good thing you can do with your body is make a living off it, thus providing a nice vehicle for your soul.

1

The Human Guinea Pig

The History of Drug Testing

Fifty years ago, drug testing consisted of putting a compound in a bottle, making a claim and seeing if it helped or hurt anybody who slugged it down. That situation began to change in September of 1937 when a new drug called "Elixir Sulfanilamide" went on the market and killed 100 people in 15 states. It turned out the stuff contained diethylene glycol, the sweet-tasting chemical used in antifreeze and quite poisonous to people. Congress was moved to pass the Federal Food, Drug and Cosmetic Act of 1938, which began requiring that drugs be proven safe before they could be introduced onto the market.

Not that this helped a whole lot.

In the 1930's a group of about 400 black men were diagnosed as having syphilis. Instead of telling them about their infection, public health officials decided to release them onto the streets for "study." As years passed, and a cure for the disease was discovered, nobody felt like telling the men, who deteriorated over the next four decades. The study was not cancelled until the 1970s.

In 1963, some other curious doctors in a New York hospital took advantage of a group of enfeebled old people to see what might happen if live cancer cells were injected just beneath the skin. Once again the patients were not fully informed as to just what was going on. Luckily, the experiment "failed" and nobody got cancer.

But it was the horrors of Nazi experimentation during World War Two that sparked the laws that protect test subjects today. From those tragedies came the "Nuremberg Code," then in the fifties, the "Helsinki Principles" that guide experimentation on human beings today. In the United States these laws have been further codified in the Code of Federal Regulations. A professional human guinea pig should be familiar with the laws that protect him and regulate drug testing on humans. A copy of the current federal law regarding human test subjects is provided in Appendix One.

Testing on human beings consists of three phases. Phase One is normally conducted after animal experiments have shown the compound fairly safe (in the short term, but not the long term). By "fairly safe," I mean it has been shown to be non-fatal in at least two species of animal.

Usually groups of fewer than 100 healthy males at one or more testing sites nationwide are then dosed with the drugs to see if they cause any harm. Once safety is determined, Phase Two studies test the drug's effectiveness on people who have the actual condition the drug was designed to treat. If these tests are successful, then much larger studies of a few thousand people are carried out in Phase Three to determine proper dosage and look for any undiscovered problems. At this point, the drug can be put on the market, but further testing may be done in Phase Four tests to measure a drug's efficacy against existing treatments or otherwise explore a drug's effects. Part One of this book focuses on the Phase One study since this is where we find the true "Human Guinea Pig."

Phase One Studies

Phase One is perhaps the most problematic for drug companies, since the only thing a test subject has to gain is money — or perhaps a warm sense that he is helping society. Since there are fortunes to be made on pharmaceuticals and so many new drugs to test, pharmaceutical companies cannot afford to wait for altruism to bring them human guinea pigs. They have to hire them.

It is not a regular job in any sense of the word, nor is it anything like being an independent contractor. In these studies, people are asked to agree to be dosed with a compound under conditions dictated by the *sponsor* and the *investigator* and which cannot be negotiated. The sponsor of the study is the drug company whose drug is being tested and the investigator is the facility that has agreed to conduct the tests. Sometimes they are one and the same, but normally they are separate entities. More on this later.

To minimize abuse of people in Phase One studies, the government has established certain principles that must be followed:

• Risks to the patient must be reasonable in relation to expected gains from the research. Patients must be fully informed of the risks they take. Researchers are required to answer any of a participant's questions about the study. Consent must be absolutely voluntary.

• It is for this last reason that prisoners are not used as test subjects in exchange for time off their sentences. Nor are extravagant sums of money offered for any testing, since both of these could be construed as coercive. Further, test participants are allowed to stop their participation at any time and for any reason. But doing so can cost you a lot of money (more on this later).

• Even though the FDA does not require that researchers compensate test subjects for any damage done to the human guinea pig, they are at least required to inform them of what compensation they may or may not provide. Generally, better facilities agree to compensate anyone injured in one of their experiments, either by taking care of them in their own facilities or paying the insurance company. They do not offer any cash payments and hence no incentives for becoming injured.

There are some exceptions to the consent rule, but these are mainly in cases where a person's life is in imminent danger and gaining consent is not possible. Also, the military has managed to interpret its duty to fully inform soldiers that they are receiving experimental drugs fairly liberally. But then again, you're in the military and your ass belongs to them, as they say. See CFR 50, sub part B § 50.23 (in Appendix One) for details on consent exemptions.

Despite the safeguards, there can still be abuses. Among them are "renegade" experiments performed by private individuals. These can be extremely dangerous, since the researchers don't have the person's welfare at heart and there are no safeguards. This book also provides tips on how to avoid these tests, or how to safeguard yourself should you decide to participate in such a study.

And sometimes (surprise!) the government itself has been known to get out of hand with drug experimentation. In the '50s and '60s the CIA ran their famous mind control experiments under a program code-named MK ULTRA. In these experiments, unsuspecting people were dosed with

LSD and other mind-altering drugs and then secretly observed — sometimes over a period of days. Some people in Canada were placed in sensory deprivation tanks and heavily dosed with LSD and barbiturates while they listened to recorded messages designed to change their personalities. This research was funded and directed by the CIA. At the same time, the CIA funded many other LSD and peyote experiments carried out in a completely above-board manner at universities around the country, turning on a generation.

Why Human Guinea Pigs?

At any given time, there are thousands of investigational drug trials being conducted all over the country. At universities, drug companies and private centers, human beings — mostly healthy males between the ages of 18 and 50 — are renting their bodies to science. In these trials, people are dosed with compounds never used on a human before. Other people are getting drugs in amounts or combinations never before tried. Perhaps a new formula has been dreamed up, but the docs need to find out if it really works. It is during Phase One that scientists study how a drug is absorbed, metabolized and excreted by the human body. Still other tests measure specific reactions to a drug, or even a food, under certain conditions. Some tests are simply to establish a baseline for future tests — a person may have his heartbeat monitored 24 hours a day for a month merely for informational purposes.

But the majority of these trials are to establish one thing: toxicity. These are the people who find out whether a substance kills a human being or not, whether or not it will cause convulsions or make you puke or hallucinate or break out in hives or anything else. Studies to determine therapeutic doses will come later — if the drug passes these first trials. One third of the drugs do not. They are simply too poisonous for human consumption.

Anything sold for human consumption has been through studies like these. They are required of all products and chemicals humans may come into contact with — from anti-depressants to adult diapers, from mosquito repellent to heart medication. Some of these studies are dangerous, some of them merely uncomfortable, most of them are boring, but all of them pay between $25 to $100 and more per day... plus room and board. They also give participants the chance to experience firsthand the effects of drugs that are still years away from the marketplace. This can be a lot of fun if you get with a study examining the effects of a pill-form of THC or a new kind of synthetic morphine. You may spend your days in relative bliss, writing world-class poetry and smiling at angelic nurses. It may not be quite so exciting if you happen to be one of the lucky ones trying out a new laxative and your days are filled with pain and cramping and filling-up little plastic cups with stool samples or having your asshole inspected four times a day by a laconic doctor in a white lab coat. On the plus side, generally, the more uncomfortable you are, the more you get paid.

It is possible to make a decent living doing this sort of "work." One professional test subject described it as "like riding a rodeo circuit" going from town to town, hospital to hospital with unemployment or vacation between. Like being a sailor, human guinea pigs get paid in large chunks just as they leave the job. Some guys will immediately go out and blow it in the nearest bar. Some use their brains and live quite well. Being a human guinea pig is an ideal profession for those who like to travel and experience new things. It doesn't matter how much education you have, all you need is a willingness to explore. The work is free from office politics or ladder climbing, there is no need to "look busy" for some atrocious boss, or otherwise abase yourself and it gives you lots of time to read or write, to improve your mind. Your body can be improved, too. Since your health is carefully scrutinized by doctors all the time, you'll have a very good handle on how your body is functioning.

The Pay

As I wrote above, prisoners or unwitting dupes used to be all the rage as test subjects until the late 1940's when it was generally decided that forcing or tricking people to become human guinea pigs was unacceptable. Prisoners are no longer used to test drugs in exchange for time off their sentences, because it is regarded as inherently coercive. Today's human guinea pig must consent to the test, be informed as to all of its aspects and potential dangers — and he must be paid.

But not too much. Too much money would also be considered coercive, so investigators face a real problem of offering enough money to entice someone to voluntarily give up his freedom for a period of as much as two months, swallow noxious substances, get stuck with needles around the clock and say thank you for it. At the same time they cannot offer too much money, since this may create a situation "too good to refuse" — especially for a poor or otherwise desperate person. So pay rates vary widely in the Phase One business and are governed by a number of factors — not the least of them the economic condition of the surrounding area and competition from other Phase One facilities.

Testing facilities have a real interest in getting participants to complete the studies. If a subject drops out before the end of the experiment, that means inconclusive results and the probability of starting over — at great expense in both time and money. To get you to finish the study, investigators turn to creative methods of payment.

Some places use sliding scales, increasing the amount of money a subject gets per day as the experiment progresses. Other places offer completion bonuses to induce people to stay with a study. These bonuses can be more than $15 per day and amount to a nice chunk for a 55-day study. Still other places may induce test subjects to finish a study by not paying a subject anything at all should he quit the test or get thrown out for some reason. All this is legal.

You should understand completely the terms of your pay agreement before you begin. Generally a facility will pay a subject for his time if he is forced to quit because something has gone wrong with the test and the investigators decide to terminate him for scientific reasons. But if the guinea pig quits on his own volition — even if it's because of a problem caused by the test — he risks a substantial cut in pay. This is not always true, but you should be aware of the possibility. I know of one guinea pig who was testing an antibiotic and broke out into hives so painful he could not continue. Although the doctors offered to lower the dosage for him, he still felt he could not go on. In that case, the scientists were interested enough in the drug that they paid him in full for the study and even offered him $100 if he would come back for another examination in a week.

On the other hand, you might think you can't take the persistent nausea caused by a compound, until you find new strength by remembering you'll receive just $35 for 12 days of hellish testing if you quit. Or perhaps nothing at all.

Normally you will be paid by check or cash. Often you'll be able to cash your check on the spot. No taxes are taken out, but the income is reported to the IRS. Oh, and by the way — you cannot bargain for better pay with these guys.

The Sites

Some facilities are ad hoc affairs that operate almost as a sideline of medical schools. Others are run on a for-profit basis. Still others are run by the drug companies themselves. Some operations throw the guinea pigs together in huge communal dormitories, while others provide semi-private rooms and VCRs. Some facilities may have as few as a half-dozen beds, while others, like Pharmakinetics in

Baltimore, have upwards of 150 beds on multiple floors and can conduct several studies at the same time.

There are advantages and disadvantages to every facility regarding comfort, pay, and the type of people you will be working with. All of these things are important to the professional guinea pig. Unfortunately, the extreme secrecy surrounding Phase One trials makes it tough to evaluate ahead of time whether a particular site is any good. Generally, though, you can make these assumptions about a study site: if it's affiliated with a university, it's likely to be a small operation with a fairly relaxed atmosphere, you may not have a lot of privacy, but you won't be harassed as much by dollar-conscious employers. You may even develop a sense of camaraderie with other guinea pigs and the staff. If you work for a large, for-profit unit, you will get less tolerance for your personality quirks, but they will do their best to keep you content enough to stay. The food will be better, the activities more varied and plentiful.

A Word About Secrecy

Drug companies and the testing companies they contract with hate to give out any information about themselves. They do not communicate with each other in any sort of professional way (that they admit to), and they normally require that their personnel and anybody who works with them (including the guinea pigs) keep their mouths shut about what goes on. They do not normally allow outsiders to even see the inside of their facilities, nor do they allow pictures to be taken. Some have armed guards posted at the doors. It is not uncommon for subjects to be searched before they begin the test, or for random shakedowns and urine tests to be given to participants during the course of the experiment. Even though all this makes the whole business sound suspicious, the caginess and paranoia is not because these guys are doing anything wrong or illegal. It all has to do with company secrets, which is to say, money. There is so much money to be made in pharmaceuticals and so much at stake that no company can risk letting its competitors know anything at all about what they are doing.

As soon as a firm believes it has discovered a compound worth investigating (only about one in 10,000 end up as medicines) it must file a patent on it. That patent protects their rights for 17 years but the first eight to ten will be eaten up by testing. As soon as a drug goes off patent, competitors can begin manufacturing it as a "generic," at a far lower price. Thus a drug company only has perhaps six or seven years in which to recoup the average $230 million it spends to develop a drug and make a profit.

During the testing period, speed and secrecy are everything. A drug in Phase One is still years from the marketplace, but will have already soaked up millions in research money. By filing the patent, the company has made itself somewhat vulnerable, since competing companies have a good idea of what's going on and can try to copy the work. Obviously, to a competitor, any information about the drug at all is helpful — whether it works, what problems may have cropped up, even the proposed name can give clues about the new drug or its marketing strategy.

Drug companies want to get their wares to market as fast as they can, with as little competition as possible. Phase One tests expose their product to the general public, perhaps for the first time. Sponsors of an investigational drug study are as protective as mother bears.

Human guinea pigs are in a position to know a lot about a drug. For one thing, test subjects are informed of the name of the company making the drug, the name of the drug, and its proposed uses. Further, all test subjects are informed about the probable effects and side effects. They might even be told detailed information about the development of the drug and its chemical basis. In order that a test subject be able to give informed consent, he must be told as much about the drug as possible, more than he may even be able to understand, and certainly more than drug companies would like to reveal.

During the experiment guinea pigs will undoubtedly at least overhear snippets of salient information other companies would love to know. That's why most guinea pigs are asked to sign something promising not to discuss their test with anyone other than those people directly involved. These promises extend beyond completion of the study, although companies don't bother to check up on you after the test to see if you're blabbing anything. Those contemplating a career as a human guinea pig should keep this in mind.

How a Drug Becomes Legal

Once a pharmaceutical company has isolated a compound it thinks will be useful for humans, it runs some basic tests on animals to prove to the FDA that the substance shows promise of effectiveness and that it is not highly poisonous. It then files an Investigational New Drug application (IND) with the FDA and can begin its human trials within 30 days, unless the FDA gives them the go-ahead to begin earlier or puts the experiments on "clinical hold" until further questions can be answered. The IND contains a plan for the study, a detailed description of the drug, and information on animal tests and manufacturing processes.

Most pharmaceutical companies have need for outside help in conducting these first experiments on humans, and contract with a facility which will conduct the test for them. Often this is a university, which not only makes a little bit of money by supervising the tests, but also gains exposure to new drugs and treatments that may be as much as ten years away from the marketplace. Hospitals, too, will conduct Phase One tests for the same reasons. Then there are companies that make it their business to turn a profit conducting these experiments.

Both hospitals and medical schools are also eager to get involved in Phases Two and Three of drug testing for more scientific reasons, but since these trials are more therapeutic and generally don't pay anything, we will leave them out of this book. On the other hand, if you suffer from some illness or disorder, it might well be worth your time to look into participation in Phase Two and Three trials. Participation here can expose you to effective treatments years before they would normally become available. Best of all, the medical care you receive is free and if the drug is effective, the company is required to provide it to you free of charge until it is approved for sale.

There are many people living better lives today because they got involved with these studies, and not only people with horrible diseases or terminal cancer... ulcer medications, migraine medications, drugs to fight allergies and depression have all become available to thousands of people long before even your doctor found out about them.

Institutional Review Boards

Every facility conducting Phase One experiments, be it a university or private company or hospital, is overseen by an Institutional Review Board (IRB). An IRB is composed of at least five people from different backgrounds (not just doctors) including one who has no affiliation with the institution at all. Most IRBs try to reflect some kind of racial or ethnic diversity and it's not at all uncommon to find some sort of mainstream religious figure serving there just to lend a holy air to the group and deflect any charges of cold-heartedness. It is the IRB's job to approve, disapprove, or recommend changes in a pharmaceutical company's *protocol* (this is the term used for the experiment and its procedures) to ensure that the human guinea pigs' rights are respected.

As you can imagine, IRBs often suggest changes in the protocol, but they are not often of much substance. Usually they require things that might help to set a guinea pig's mind at ease (explaining that, although blood will be drawn often, the total volume may only be a few ounces, detailing what sort of precautions have been taken should anything go wrong, etc.). The IRB also makes sure the testing facility isn't getting ripped off — for instance, pharmaceutical companies are not normally permitted to make a profit off the tests or to charge the researchers for the product. That doesn't stop IRB members from being paid for their time and trouble, however, but this is paid as a "consulting fee" not a salary.

2

On The Job

How To Find A Phase One Study

Since Phase One facilities don't even communicate with each other, much less the outside world, they can be somewhat difficult to track down. Phase One facilities don't meet in Las Vegas every year for a trade show on the latest in human experimentation. Indeed, a testing facility may not even view itself as a part of anything larger than itself. And, in many cases, a site is not always conducting a study. For instance, a university's Study Unit may run a bioavailability study on a new pain killer for several months, then run no tests at all for several months. Some hospitals and teaching institutions are interested only in certain types of drugs that benefit programs of special interest (hypertension medication, anti-depressants, etc.) and may pass up chances to run other kinds of tests.

Other places, especially the for-profit outfits, are aggressively on the lookout both for drugs to test and test subjects. Because of this it can be worth it to make a trip to, say, Baltimore just to wait for something to come up at Pharmakinetics or any of a number of sites in that city. Once you've successfully completed a study with a certain facility, they are likely to find another one for you as soon as you qualify. In the meantime you'll be in the neighborhood of a number of hospitals and clinics.

The same thing goes for many other cities. In Appendix Two, I have provided an extensive list of private testing facilities. Although I've managed to round up the names, addresses and phone numbers of more than 150 of them, the list probably represents no more than a fifth of the study sites currently in operation. It does not necessarily include smaller non-profit oriented sites. Also, many companies operate facilities in different towns and states and this list doesn't give much information about any branches or subsidiaries — just the home office. A single call may get you information about two or more testing sites. If you feel like letting your fingers do the walking, you can use the list to map out a cross-country spree of human guinea piggery that should put you well on your way to financial independence, if not vast wealth.

A newsletter called *Pills-A-Go-Go* (*The Journal of Pills*), regularly publishes valuable information about new drugs and investigational drug studies under way both in the United States and overseas. The rag comes out every couple of months and costs $12 per year to subscribe. The address is: 1202 E. Pike Street #849, Seattle, WA 98122.

One of the best ways to quickly locate a study near you is to look for an ad in the newspaper. Often the student newspaper near any of these facilities will run ads touting human guinea pigging as a good way to make extra money — much like plasma collection centers do. Another way is to wander around the hallways of medical schools looking on bulletin boards for tests, since medical students are often targeted for the jobs.

And don't forget to go through the psychology building — psychology students are constantly looking for test subjects for short-duration experiments, many involving alcohol. These tests don't normally pay too well (say $10 or $15) but they only take a couple of hours, so they don't interfere too much with regular life. Be advised, however, that these psychological experiments frequently involve deception. The experimenters don't always tell the subjects what's really going on, so they can get a more accurate picture of human behavior. For instance, you may be told that you will be watching a series of pictures and noting your reactions when, in actuality, the experiment involves monitoring your behavior as you wait with a group of students. Although these tests may involve drinking a shot or two of alcohol or perhaps enduring a mild electric shock, they aren't going to do any damage to you. Generally the people running these tests are interested in getting finished so they can write their papers and relax.

Phase One drug tests are entirely different. There is no deception going on. You are not being secretly tested for anything. Unless they tell you it's a possibility, you're also not getting a placebo. Once again, it's all up front.

Another way to find tests is to get courted by a recruiter. Sometimes Phase One recruiters can be found in downtown missions, soup kitchens or other places where poor people hang out. They have been known to cruise shopping malls handing out flyers to likely candidates. This is especially true if the company needs a particular age/race/sex group. In fact, it is rumored that certain drug companies make a big philanthropic show of funding a local shelter for the homeless while using it as a sort of guinea pig farm for their drug studies.

Studies can be located by hooking up with specialists who may know of drug studies pertaining to their fields. In this case, your best bet is to contact a hospital or unit in a hospital known for a specific type of medicine. Your own physician may be aware of a number of studies taking place or about to take place and be able to direct you to one.

It is futile to call the FDA to find out about tests. Although the FDA knows about all of them, it is forbidden to release information about ongoing studies without the sponsor's permission. Fat chance of that ever happening.

Calling up drug companies and asking where they're testing new drugs is likely to get you nowhere. Still, the names and addresses of practically all the drug companies operating in the U.S. are listed in the *Physician's Desk Reference* (PDR) and correlating their locations with test sites can give you an idea of what company you'll be guinea pigging for as well as what types of drugs you'll be taking. For instance, Abbott Laboratories is headquartered in North Chicago, so a test site in the Chicago area might easily be doing tests for that company. When you look through the catalog of drugs made by Abbott, you'll find they make damn near everything, but not much in the way of narcotics. Tranquilizers, sure, amphetamines, they make them too. But no super pain-killers.

Other drug companies tend to stick to certain areas — a lot of psychotropic drugs are made by Sandoz, and Roche. Burroughs-Wellcome seems to make a lot of drugs for infections and viruses, although lately they've been branching out. Since Burroughs is located in Research Triangle Park, North Carolina, don't be surprised if that's where you'll find some new anti-viral concoction being tested at one of the sites.

Using this information, you might be able to latch onto the type of study you would like to get into, by looking up which drug manufacturers make which drugs, then pinpointing Phase One sites in that general area. Once again, leafing through the *PDR* and cross-checking against the list. If you read, for instance, in *Pills-A-Go-Go* that Ciba-Geigy is working on a new compound to increase the duration of an orgasm, and you want to get in on it, then head for the New Jersey sites.

One of the best ways to find out about studies is to get in on one. Once on the "inside," your fellow guinea pigs will be able to fill you in on their experiences. You may even run across underground lists of upcoming studies that get photocopied and distributed among guinea pigs at different testing sites. This information has the advantage of being current. Some guinea pigs use this information to travel from one study to the next without much interruption.

If you live in a big city or university town, you should have access to a large library which subscribes to newspapers from around the country. Make sure to scour these for test ads. These are the most valuable contacts you can make, because the person on the other end will be happy to talk to you frankly about what tests they are running and, more importantly, which tests may be coming up in the future. Thus, you can plan a little bit. You may miss out on the particular test being conducted at the time but have some advance knowledge of another test coming up. A good time to make this type of search is during the lag time between being accepted for a test and actually beginning the study. This is often as long as two weeks.

Working Conditions

One professional test subject described participating in a study as "like being in jail only you're getting paid." This is an apt description. Phase One facilities are not resorts and the scientists are not interested in you as a person. They only love you for your body. When you enter a study, you'll have to wear a name bracelet. While in a study you must eat, sleep, or do anything else they tell you to do and you must do it instantly. If they tell you to go to sleep at 12:00, then they do not mean 12:01. This is difficult for many first-timers to understand and they run the risk of disrupting the study and either getting thrown out of a study or being blackballed if they resist. Tests have to be tightly controlled and everything must be timed to get FDA approval. That means the *facility* will control your body — not you. Pharmaceutical companies are interested in precise data and tight results. Every piece of data must be verified by the facility. Facilities that fail to do this go out of business quickly. Studies can last from 48 hours to more than two months, and during this time your primary job is to be a human body and obey the personnel.

It is this need for uniformity and control that dominates the atmosphere of a test. Realize this from the beginning and you will have little difficulty. Don't try to sneak in any drugs or even food. Do not hassle the nurses or anybody else, including your fellow guinea pigs. Getting thrown out is a drastic measure not only for you but for the facility; after all, losing a patient means less exacting test information. If you jeopardize the experiment they will have no choice. Just do as you're told. I stress this point only because of the severity of the penalty for being thrown out: a huge loss of money and a potential loss of career. Statistics show that 92.5% of participants complete their studies. About 3.5% are dropped for medical reasons (in which case they are paid pro rata for their time and effort). Only 4% are dropped for "non-compliance."

Typically, a Phase One study will take place on a single floor in a building. The floor will contain sleeping rooms, bathrooms, a lounge area and a small cafeteria. Other floors are devoted to doctors' offices, examination rooms or laboratories. You'll probably spend the entire time on one floor, share a room and eat in a small cafeteria. Some of the less comfortable places cram you into large sleeping rooms with lots of bunk beds, while other places give you more privacy. Often there is a telephone in your room, but you won't be able to make long distance calls with it. For that you'll have to use a pay phone located somewhere on the floor. Smart guinea pigs should remember to bring a few rolls of quarters for long distance calls.

The area where you live is hospital-like — that is, clean and somewhat sterile-looking. Very often there will be a recreation room with a pool table or chess boards or the like. There will also be a day room or lounge area where you and the other guinea pigs can sit around drinking coffee (if allowed) while waiting to get stabbed by a nurse. You'll find that the conversation will rarely concentrate on the study, in this way being a human guinea pig is very much like being an inmate. Conversations revolve around what you'll do with the money you earn, what you have planned after getting out, not why you're there. On longer studies you can expect to get restless as the completion date nears and you become a short-timer. Unfortunately, this is a time to be especially careful not to start breaking rules. By this time you've provided plenty of (albeit somewhat incomplete) data and the staff will be even less inclined to take guff, even as you feel more inclined to give it.

You will live very closely with the other test subjects, something you must consider before participating. You may have to take your showers with these guys in a communal gang shower at the same time every day. You will have to eat with these guys, shit with these guys, converse with these guys, some of whom are lacking intelligence and can become downright annoying. If your roommate snores — tough shit. If you get horny, you'll have to use some ingenuity to find a place to beat off with some privacy. Perhaps you and your roommate can work something out.

Do not engage in sex with the other guinea pigs, even if you are a homosexual. Wait until you get out. That will definitely get you into trouble if you get caught.

Your day is structured by the protocol. It may be as simple as being dosed in the morning with a drug and then having a blood test in the afternoon, or it may be that you will have as many as 18 blood draws in a 24 hour period. You may be required to wear electrodes or a special harness to hold some sort of measuring device. In the case of mosquito repellent, yes, you will have to be exposed to mosquitos and endure a certain number of bites. All dosing is done by staff, so that means if you're testing a suppository, you'll get it inserted by a nurse or doctor every day you're on the study.

Scientists love to look at your bodily fluids and there is no fluid they disdain — blood, tears, sputum, urine, stool — they're all fair game. You may be required to submit to an endoscopy (having an optical device in a tube shoved down your throat and into your stomach so the doctor can examine the stomach walls) or a thorough search of your colon with a device about a mile long. But you will know about this ahead of time, and steps will be taken to minimize any unnecessary discomfort. There will be no surprises. What you do in between blood draws or trips to the mosquito chamber is up to you... sort of.

Remember, drug companies are looking for average people leading average lives. That means no special exercise is allowed (although part of the protocol might easily call for exhaustive stints on a treadmill) so don't plan on getting in shape while on a study. Expect your muscles to atrophy. Doing some non-exhaustive isometric exercises is permissible. Learn to keep your muscles in tone by simply flexing your muscles or raising yourself slowly off the chair an inch or two and lowering yourself back down. There are plenty of books you can pick up on this subject.

Your biggest problem is boredom and the facilities don't often do much to help you alleviate it. In fact, some studies seem designed to drive you insane. A study might require you to remain lying down, motionless, 18 hours a day. Some may deprive you of sleep for a night or two. Some studies could have you eating nothing but carbohydrates, or any other special diet you can think of. In fact, a lot of guinea pigs prefer the more uncomfortable experiments involving frequent blood draws etc., simply to break up the monotony of a day. And many studies can be a lot of fun, especially if the drug you're taking has the potential for mind-alteration. In that case, you may be dosed with a medication and then required to perform certain tasks to test your motor skills, or to take psychological examinations to establish what effects the drug is having.

Facilities vary on what you are allowed to bring with you to keep you occupied during your stay. I've never heard of a study that did not allow people to bring books with them, although they will be searched for contraband. Generally, the place will make some effort to provide books, although you may find the selection is limited and boring. Few studies will allow you to bring your own video tapes, but almost all of them provide a VCR, Nintendo game and their own tapes (once again, these tend to be fairly innocuous). Some provide hokey activities like macrame or lanyard weaving, but if you get bored enough, these otherwise tedious projects can become amazingly absorbing and interesting.

Writing is always a possibility and many places will allow you to bring a lap top computer for that purpose, although a typewriter may be considered too disruptive (ditto a printer for your computer). Test facilities have seen it all before, so don't try to bring in your welding equipment or band saw. You can also leave your cello at home. It all goes back to the smoothness of the study. One well-known test site used to allow people to bring in small tool kits to work on models... until some bozo decided to amuse himself by taking his bed apart.

But plain old writing on paper is allowed and you can send and receive mail. Once again, anything coming to you from the outside is liable to be searched. Listening to music on headphones is permissible in some places and drawing and perhaps working with clay are also possibilities. By far the best thing you can do is bring enough books to read — even for a short study. Since your whole world may consist of just a few hundred square feet, the floor can quickly grow tiresome and books offer a handy escape. If possible, have someone on the outside you can call to bring you something if you need it. But you can forget food. There is no canteen where you can buy a bag of Chips Ahoy or a Yoo Hoo. Some places may provide art supplies and take the money from your pay, but don't count on it. Once again, there is nothing resort-like about a Phase One testing site.

You will not be allowed to leave the facility without permission or unescorted. You'll probably not get permission unless the situation is extraordinary, and even then someone will be required to go with you. Although some places might not make any serious attempt to physically restrain you, sneaking out is unwise. Your absence will quickly be noted and then the test is over for you.

Cameras are never allowed into a facility for fear that a shot containing some kind of sensitive information will get taken. Eli Lilly's facility in Indianapolis, for instance, is very strict about what it allows on its private floor at the county hospital. All of a guinea pig's personal belongings, including clothes, are taken away and the test subject is made to wear a special jumpsuit. No recording devices or tape players of any kind are allowed onto the floor and phone calls are monitored by Lilly personnel. The slightest hint that you are leaking any information results in termination right that minute.

On the other hand, Lilly pays pretty well and it's a comfortable setting. Word has it that its billiard table is one of the best. And they may have some interesting experiments going on. After all, it was Eli Lilly that developed a process to manufacture LSD in huge quantities, selling all of it to the U.S. military.

You are also generally not allowed any visitors, though sometimes exceptions are made on extremely long studies; even then, the visits will be under close observation. For the most part, visitors create too much of a problem for the staff and they just don't allow it. However, people *can* bring things to you by dropping them off in some outer office to be given to you later... after they are searched.

It is unfeasible for me to compile a detailed description of the various testing sites. Even this information is considered to be too sensitive to permit the competition to know. So until you get inside, it's guesswork. What I have provided here are general conditions you can expect, but things change. For all I know, Lilly has trashed their pool table and fired a lot of their surly security guards. Perhaps some other facility has instituted a stricter no visitors policy. All of them are free to change the rules as long as they do not mistreat you. Facilities also undergo expansion and remodelling, something that can substantially alter conditions. Since the drug business has been so good in these last few years, many have done exactly that. What was once a human warehouse may now be a pretty plush establishment with private cable TV in every room.

However, any potential human guinea pig can get a pretty good idea of what awaits him by talking to the recruiter, who is likely to be very up front about current conditions and policies. This is the best information possible, along with current tidbits you can gain from other guinea pigs once you're in the circuit.

Your Fellow Guinea Pigs

First of all, as you look around, it'll be just you and the boys. The vast majority of test subjects are males between the ages of 18 and 50. This is because drug companies don't want to expose females to drugs that have never been tried before, since they may affect either the reproductive organs or any possible babies, should she be pregnant. In fact, there is evidence to suggest that some drugs are able to affect more than one generation. So, on the whole, from a liability standpoint, drug companies are unwilling to use women.

There are exceptions to this. Lately, for instance, a lot of study is being given to estrogen replacement, and consequently firms need post-menopausal women for these tests. Most birth control drugs are also girls-only tests. Other tests are open to both men and women if there is no compelling reason to exclude females — if the study is merely to establish norms of basic bodily functions, for instance. There are even controlled studies done on the absorption of nutrients, for which both men and women are needed. Mosquito repellent, too, has to be tested on both men and women.

Some studies also call for specialized groups of people who are otherwise healthy except for having high cholesterol, high blood pressure, cirrhosis, varying degrees of kidney failure or who are elderly. But once again, what is mostly needed in Phase One testing are healthy men.

Studies are done on groups of 12 to 24 people. These groups can be smaller or larger, but it is unlikely that you'll be in a facility with more than 50 people (and not all of them will be participating in the same experiment). In some places, especially in a university setting, the atmosphere can be quite convivial and you could end up with some valuable friendships in addition to your filthy lucre.

Guinea pigs in the experiment will represent the population around the site. If you are in a Boston hospital, you will likely find urban unemployed people, men who have seasonal work or drifters. Nearer to a college campus, you'll be among students or those who continue to hang out in a college town. You can use these demographics to your advantage in picking a study. College towns are great places to look for studies during the school year when students can't afford to take any time off, but horrible during the summer when so many jobless bodies are available for injection, rejection, and dejection at a test facility. Similarly, economic slumps clog up spaces at urban drug study facilities. It's better to hit cities during prosperous times or holidays when folks like to be home with their families.

It may happen that some personal friction develops between you and another guinea pig. In this situation you must do whatever you can to avoid that person and relieve the tension. There are, however, jerks who gain a real sense of satisfaction from bothering people. This jerk may even be your roommate, putting you in a difficult situation. The best thing to do is confront this person privately and talk about the problem. Explain how you feel and suggest a remedy (he should stop whistling or telling bad jokes or whatever). Tell him your next step will be to go to someone supervising the study to fix the problem, which will jeopardize both of your positions. Make an honest effort to make friends — you're trapped in there with him and there's no way to escalate the fight while on the study. If you must, agree that you hate each other and make an appointment to beat the shit out of each other once the study is over. Don't laugh, I've seen it done.

If you really want, you can go to the authorities but they will not like being bothered by your personal problems, and changing roommates is a hassle that will cause them to have to change records, timetables and a lot of other things. This should be your last resort.

The Screening Process

Those in charge of a study do more than double check your blood type. Your appearance and personality are also scrutinized to make sure you'll fit in. Investigators generally like to have a mix of regulars and new people, as well as people they feel will get along. Keep this in mind whenever talking to a recruiter or anybody involved in the screening process. Speak positively about yourself and about others, make sure you are clean and you've brushed your teeth. A guy who drags himself in from an alley somewhere and is picking lint out of his hair is not a good candidate. Show that you can articulate yourself well enough that they'll have faith in any subjective evaluations you may be called upon to make such as whether a drug makes you feel euphoric or hallucinate. Don't be aggressive and by all means don't swear. Do your best to appear bright and cheerful.

Tell the truth. You will be hard-pressed to second-guess the doctors about what they're looking for and they will check your answers anyway. You'll be given a complete physical examination, so it is pointless to hide any medical condition that might exclude you. Getting caught lying at the very least makes you appear unreliable. Remember, you are no more than a living test tube for these guys. They don't give a shit about your politics, religion, or anything else. If you have already participated in experiments, by all means say so. That just means you understand some of the ground rules. If you've never done it before, tell them that, too. A freshman is often putty in the facility's hands and is less likely to try to push the limits of the rules.

The researchers are obligated to explain in detail what they are planning to do and what they are looking for. You will be informed about the effects of the drug, including its potential dangers. You'll also be informed of any possible benefits you might derive from the experiment. This is one place where it is permissible to ask questions. Ask anything you like now, especially about those things that worry you. I know one guinea pig who has even managed to get physicians to show him raw data obtained from animal tests. Investigators are careful to ensure that you give informed consent. Don't worry about bothering them, that's what this part of the process is for and many scientists get off on talking about their projects to people they think appreciate it.

One of the beneficial aspects of this process is the scrutinizing physical examination you will undergo if chosen for the study. By the end of this process you can be sure you're not carrying any bizarre diseases, dying of cancer, or even have mild ailments. Guinea pigs must be healthy!

Not everyone who considers himself healthy is healthy enough for a drug study, however. A little less than half of the applicants for a particular study will be turned down for a variety of reasons, chiefly drug use, recent plasma/blood donation, being overweight, or even being a vegetarian. Once again, drug companies need Joe Average. Anything you can do to fit the stereotype will help.

Those that get past the initial screening process will face additional diagnostic tests that will disqualify about one in three. Reasons include elevated liver function (do not go on a drinking binge before recruitment), abnormal urinalysis, low hematocrit or a low white cell count.

Also, for various reasons a small percentage drop out before the study begins. Drop-outs are pretty rare once the study has begun.

It should be noted that being rejected from a study for something like an elevated liver function result does not preclude you from trying again. These things are not considered permanent and it's worth your time to come back again and again if necessary until you "pass." It should go without saying that a proper diet and adequate sleep as well as abstinence from drugs and alcohol will help you pass. To this end, I suggest you read up a bit on nutrition and follow a good diet. Some suggestions for improving blood test scores are given later in the chapter.

There are certain reasons for automatic exclusion from any test. Generally:

• Subjects should not have taken any other prescription drugs within the preceding two weeks, no matter if it's a pill, a skin cream, injection or something inhaled.

• Intravenous use of any illicit drugs within the previous ten years is grounds for permanent exclusion at some facilities.

• If you have used any illicit drugs within the previous six months you'll be required to pass a drug test to make sure you're clean now.

• If you say you're a non-smoker, be prepared to prove it with a pee test prior to dosing and at any time during the study.

• People who are missing any of the "double" organs such as eyes, kidneys, etc. are permanently excluded. (Remember this, in case you decide to sell your kidney. This could ruin your career as a human guinea pig.)

• If you've ever had a stomach operation or any other type of operation on your gastro-intestinal tract, you may be permanently excluded because of the possibility of altered drug absorption.

• Mental or emotional problems, which have required in-patient hospitalization can get you permanently excluded. Out-patient mental patients must be at least 5 years without medication.

• Any other reason the investigator thinks up, including your attitude.

Passing the Medical Exams

Once you get past the major hurdles (not being a junkie or obese or something) the investigators will want to take samples of your blood and urine for diagnostic testing. About one out of three "flunk" these tests for a variety of reasons — elevated liver functions, blood in urine, abnormal amounts of white or red blood cells, blood volume, etc.

These tests yield clinical data that is impossible for you to tamper with — they give an accurate reading of your health at the time the blood/urine is collected, and suggest patterns of general health. Still, there are a few ways you can minimize your chances of flunking blood and urine tests.

The first and best way to ensure good test results is to watch what you take in, since this is always and immediately reflected in the blood. This means you should not do anything abnormal. You may believe that taking 20,000 IUs of vitamin A every day is improving your health, but it won't look like that to a clinician who will only notice an abnormality — probably in your liver. Mind you, it won't suggest to the investigator that you are sick, merely "abnormal," and therefore excludable.

So you should stop taking any fat-soluble vitamins at least two weeks before you plan to try out for a guinea pig position. Ditto with over-the-counter pain medications — especially acetaminophen (Tylenol) as these can be especially hard on your liver and kidneys. Drop a few Tylenols before a blood test and you may well come off looking like someone with a liver problem.

And do not go drinking alcohol the night before the study. In fact, don't drink alcohol for at least a couple of weeks before the study, since alcohol is highly destructive to lots of tissues and causes your liver, especially, to react accordingly. Even one beer the night before a blood test is enough to suggest an impaired liver.

It is also essential that you stay on a fairly low-protein diet. Eggs, especially, will contribute to the amount of protein in your urine and could easily lead the investigators to conclude that you have impaired kidney function. Drink plenty of fluids as a regular part of your diet to keep your kidneys clean. Also, take regular iron supplements along with folic acid and vitamin B-12 to keep red blood cell levels high.

You may want to conduct some tests with your doctor first and see if you've got any problems. Perhaps he may be willing to prescribe certain medications that may alter the outcome of blood and urine tests. Some blood pressure medications, for instance, may improve the performance of your kidneys. Other chemicals can mask potentially disqualifying problems.

On the whole, however, please keep in mind that these tests are not done simply to exclude you for no good reason. If you have a serious health problem, do not be so foolish as to risk getting even sicker just to get in an experiment. General good diet and adequate sleep should be all you need. Also, you may find that your blood and urine "quality" will vary over a period of a few weeks, it's not unknown for a person to be rejected for one or more studies and then suddenly be found perfectly acceptable for another.

Perhaps I should add a footnote here to the rule against lying. Obviously, if you are missing a kidney, they're going to notice. Even if you could get away with it, it's not a good idea to risk your only remaining organ for the few bucks you can make from a drug study. Kidneys play a big role in drug metabolism and some surprisingly small amounts of relatively "harmless" medications can do great damage to kidneys. Ibuprofen (Advil, etc.), for example, can do this.

But if you're certain you cannot be caught, then go ahead and lie. Just keep the lie simple and do not ever reveal to anyone, EVER, that you lied. If you even hint this to anyone at the facility, you'll be caught. Investigational drug studies involve such concentrated groups of human beings monitoring each other that the lie will be discovered. So if you shot up a few years ago and don't have any track marks, why jeopardize your livelihood with the truth? Similarly, if you did a couple of Sudafeds last weekend, go ahead and lie. But, be aware, there may be serious medical reasons for these exclusions. Monoamine Oxidase Inhibitors (a type of anti-depressant), as an example, can react violently with even small amounts of cold medications or even certain types of cheese to cause potentially fatal seizures.

3

Types of Experiments

Bioequivalence

One of the most common types of tests given by investigators is the *bioequivalence* test.

In the last ten years, many drugs have gone "generic," meaning their patents have expired and the formulas can be copied and sold by anyone. Up until 1984, all a company had to do was prove that its version of a popular drug was "bioavailable" — that it was absorbed into the body like the original drug, though perhaps not at the same rate. This is part of the reason generics have a bad name today. But in 1984 the FDA changed the rules to require generic knock-offs to be not only bioavailable but "bioequivalent" — that is, the rate of absorption and metabolism must not be significantly different from the pioneer drug.

Most of these tests have to be carried out in live human beings although some of them can be proven bioequivalent in vitro (in a test tube). Tests like this must also be done if the dosage of a drug is to be changed, so don't be surprised if you take part in a study which examines the effects of a large dose of aspirin, or of time-released vitamin C or something equally innocuous. The vast amounts of money to be made by copying successful drugs means that a lot of tests will be conducted on compounds already on sale at the local pharmacy. Valium, for instance, spawned dozens of competitors the minute it went off patent in 1984. Each one of these ersatz diazepam formulas had to prove it was just as good as Valium to get on the market — and hundreds of folks got to mellow out, write world-class poetry and smile at the nurses.

"Me Too" Drugs

The money to be made off of anxiolitics (anxiety-reducing drugs, of which Valium was an original), especially benzodiazepines, provoked widespread experimentation with the formula, to concoct drugs that were different enough to get a separate patent but had virtually the same effect. Out of the Valium battle came a string of tranquilizing drugs.

This type of drug is known as a *"me too" drug* and also accounts for lots of Phase One studies. In many ways, these are good studies since the general effects of the medicine are already known and the scientists are just making sure there isn't some biochemical glitch that will accidently turn a person into a werewolf. Among those drugs likely to be "me too" drugs are medications for high blood pressure, ulcers, high cholesterol and a class of pain medication known as non-steroidal anti-inflammatories (NSAIDs).

During these kinds of studies you will likely be jabbed with a needle at least a half dozen times per day, including during "wash out" days when you will not be dosed at all. Also you can expect to give urine samples, but probably no more than that. Although these studies are often pretty predictable, they can be a drag since some of the dosages are outside what is normally considered optimum. One guinea pig I met turned down a nice two-week study because he'd have to take ten aspirins per day. This same guinea pig didn't mind testing an anti-diarrhea medication, however, and cheerfully submitted to induced diarrhea every single morning for ten days. Once again, decide what you're comfortable with before you do a test. If you feel uneasy about it, pass it up and wait for one you can deal with. The investigators will appreciate this, too.

Tolerance

Some studies will have to do with *tolerance* of a drug and the investigators will increase the dosage of a particular substance to see what might be the maximum dose a person can tolerate. Needless to say, these studies have an inherent element of discomfort since the dosage is increased until you say "uncle" or until the investigator deems it necessary to stop for whatever reason.

Comparison Studies

Another type of test you may come across are *comparison studies* in which two or more compounds are tested at the same time to see how they react to each other. A lot of this testing is required of anything going over the counter (OTC), to make sure it doesn't react badly with common foods or other OTC medications. Sometimes a bad reaction is expected and researchers are trying to find out just how much of a therapeutic dose can be given without causing unacceptable levels of discomfort or danger. They may also be testing to see if the substance can provoke an allergic reaction, or whether or not the drug's effect is strengthened or weakened in the presence of another drug or food. Many, many studies like this are done with alcohol. For some reason, even though this drug has been around for thousands of years, it remains a mystery to scientists who never tire of getting people drunk and measuring their reactions.

Other Experiments

You may also be involved in experiments where you are dosed with drugs "marked" with *radioactivity* and their metabolism observed. You may undergo mammograms, bone density tests (painless), X-rays and other clinical tests. You may also be participating in sleep studies in which you will be closely observed as you sleep, with or without drugs.

These days, about a fourth of studies involve drugs affecting the central nervous system and another fourth are studies of the cardiovascular system. The rest of the tests are commonly studies of gastro-intestinal drugs, analgesics, anti-infectives, and cholesterol.

Another kind of experiment you may encounter will be those that test a human's reactions under certain conditions — usually without any drugs at all. Examples of this are some cold water experiments performed at the University of Minnesota at Duluth in which volunteers jumped into freezing water and stayed there for half an hour or so, or until they became unconscious. Scientists then studied the effects on the body, as well as different ways to relieve hypothermia. Of course the study was uncomfortable but each time they did it, the guinea pig got $100.

At the University of Vancouver in British Columbia, there have been extensive isolation experiments to find out what happens to people when deprived of outside stimuli to varying degrees. The experiments can range from being locked in a sound-proof room to being shut up in an isolation tank, floating in brine, and spinning into a dream world.

Remember, everything that a human can use or that might affect a human being requires testing on real people. A lot of this is done at universities. Keep this in mind when looking for experiments. Universities in Florida may have some hair-raising (but necessary) tests for shark repellent. Big city universities may have tests to determine how much and what kind of noise a person can withstand, or sleep deprivation, or exposure to heat. Keep your mind open.

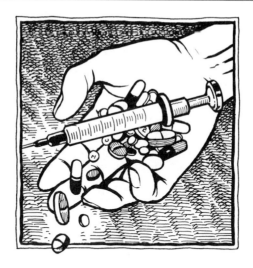

4

Basic Drugs

The following is a compendium of the drug/substance categories you will likely encounter in Phase One testing. By reading each one you will have a basic understanding of the particular classification of drug/substance you will come into contact with. I include this section because, despite the pains taken by investigators to explain to guinea pigs what they're dosing them with, I have often noticed that the guys still seem to be a bit fuzzy about just what's going on. Some of them appear to have no understanding of the drugs they're taking at all. As a human guinea pig, you owe it to yourself to find out as much as you can about the study you're participating in — if for no other reason than to make the study more interesting. Later on, when a "miracle drug" hits the market, you may be able to recognize it as one you helped to test.

Further, this information could come in handy down the line when evaluating your medical history. A man who's been shot up with hormones, large doses of nutrients, CNS depressants, etc. should definitely know what the possible consequences are. I am not suggesting that you will be harmed by any of these tests, merely that they will have some bearing on your future health. Some drugs you take may have the effect of making you healthier, or protecting you from contracting some disease in the future.

This list is only a beginning. This is information that is already generally known about these basic classifications of drugs. As a human guinea pig, you may be coming into contact with drugs that not only aren't described here, but aren't described anywhere at all. Drug companies in recent years have switched their strategies from re-mixing what they've already got to targeting specific conditions they hope to cure and then inventing a molecule to fix it. They have also increasingly turned toward painstaking examination of the natural world to formulate their drugs.

Squibb "invented" an entire new line of heart medication by working with the venom of an Amazon snake. Merck Sharp & Dohme introduced a brand-new drug to lower cholesterol levels — made from a microbe they dug up in Spain! The "miracle drug" cyclosporin (which prevents organ rejection) originates from dirt found in Scandinavia! Drug researchers are combing everything from spider webs to leech saliva to guide them in their work. On the other hand, nobody's abandoned the drugs we have already and lots of tests are conducted to determine whether they can be used for anything else. Hence, the plethora of aspirin studies.

Don't be intimidated by any words you don't know. Although I've done my best to keep this simple, I haven't diluted the information to baby talk. Anything you can do to educate yourself about the human body and chemistry will help you. Start reading science magazines, flip through illustrated medical textbooks or dictionaries, watch the health channel on television. None of this stuff is too hard for you to understand.

It's also useful to get hold of a *Physician's Desk Reference* (*PDR*). This thick book is an annual compendium of every drug on the market, along with loads of chemical and prescribing information. Leafing through one of these will expose you to a lot of terms commonly used in the pharmaceutical industry. If you absorb only a few percent of what's in there, you'll be better equipped. *PDRs* can be found at used book stores or very often your doctor has an old volume or two he'll probably let you have.

Gastrointestinal Drugs

These are drugs that work on the stomach, duodenum, esophagus, and large and small intestines. Much of the work is on healing ulcers and spastic colons. Ulcers and the like used to be treated with diet and antacids but since the development of what are known as H2 antagonists such as Tagamet and Zantac, the field has changed. Instead of trying to neutralize excess acid, it is now possible to inhibit the production of acid from acid-producing cells in the stomach. The number of people with stomach troubles is huge... and so is the amount they will pay to escape the pain. Zantac, for instance, is so popular that it accounts for 50% of the revenues of the company that makes it.

Antacids

You know what these are — Maalox, Tums, etc. These work by neutralizing the acidity of the stomach by increasing the overall pH of the stomach. They also improve the muscle tone of the lower esophagus so that less acid is disgorged into your throat creating "heartburn." One of the pharmacological problems with antacids is that, by changing the environment of the stomach, they can alter the way some drugs are absorbed, decreasing the absorption of drugs like antibiotics, increasing the absorption of drugs like amphetamines. Chronic use can also lead to mineral imbalances. Antacids also affect the *bioavailibility* of other drugs.

Anticholinergic drugs

These drugs work on the Central Nervous System (CNS) to inhibit smooth muscle action and secretory glands. These reduce spasms in the GI tract, and lower acid production. They must be given in fairly large doses to have any therapeutic effect. They can easily produce drowsiness, dry mouth, blurry vision and they interact with a host of other commonly used drugs such as antidepressants and anti-histamines, usually potentiating (increasing) these uncomfortable side-effects.

H2 Antagonists

These drugs inhibit the production of stomach acid by directly affecting part of the acid-producing cells in the stomach. These have proven to be a breakthrough in ulcer-treatment and may even go over the counter within the near future (look for Phase One tests of the OTC versions!). These drugs have almost no side effects and appear to be completely non-toxic.

There are other drugs being developed along these same lines, which act on the acid-producing cells in the stomach. Patents on Tagamet and Zantac (the two most popular ones) will be expiring in the next few years, so drug companies are scrambling to make their own versions for prescription use, as well as generic versions. There will be lots of testing of these safe drugs.

Digestive enzymes

These are compounds which aid in the digestion of certain foods. Some people, for genetic reasons have difficulty digesting milk, starch, proteins, fats and/or cellulose. These drugs replace missing enzymes. In addition there are even pills that increase the acidity of the stomach for those people who don't secrete enough hydrochloric acid.

Laxatives

These drugs promote bowel movements, usually by attracting and retaining water in the intestinal tract. Some also work by stimulating or irritating the bowel. Bulk-producing laxatives like Metamucil work by sucking up water and causing the feces to bulge out against the intestines, thus inducing a bowel movement. Studies of new drugs in this area are likely to be of more physiological compounds that are not as harsh as those that work by irritation of the bowel.

Antidiarrheals

Here, as in laxatives, the trend is away from the more powerful agents. Medicines like Paregoric and other opium-derived chemicals work by essentially paralyzing the bowel and increasing "intestinal transit time." These drugs are particularly harmful if the diarrhea is caused by some sort of intestinal parasite, since the medicine gives the bugs a better chance to penetrate the intestinal walls. Today, research is being done on drugs like loperamide (Immodium) which recently has become available over the counter. These drugs work more specifically and gently on the intestine and increase the viscosity of stool.

Vaccines

It is unlikely that you will be involved in any studies of vaccines, since these drugs, to be tested, obviously require exposing test subjects to potentially lethal diseases. For these, investigators use specific volunteers who may already have the disease or are at risk of getting it. Be wary of any test for a biological agent such as a vaccine or an anti-venom. Contact the FDA for further information.

Things are different overseas. Right now there is extensive human testing of an anti-AIDS vaccine in healthy people and the FDA couldn't be more tickled. This is because all the humans are from impoverished third-world countries where nobody resembles an FDA functionary in the slightest.

Analgesics (Pain-killers)

If there's one thing Americans don't like, it's the slightest pain. Watching all those headache commercials, you'd get the impression that half of the country is constantly tortured by bone-crushing pain, mostly in the form of headaches. As a consequence, there are a lot of drugs out there designed to relieve pain. Here are a few classifications of such drugs, although this list is far from complete. Pain medications will include not only narcotics and aspirin, but muscle relaxants, anti-migraine preparations and anesthetics. These are some of the pain-killers a human guinea pig is likely to encounter. But don't be surprised if you get the opportunity to get dosed with something not listed here — or even something you never *thought* of. Remember, these guys are experimenting with Amazon snake venom!

Narcotics

These are the ones related to opium, which — it just so happens — is related to substances known as endorphins that occur naturally in our brains. Most of these, from morphine to propoxyphene (Darvocet), are alkaloids. Most of these drugs do a very effective job of eliminating pain by occupying the same receptors that endorphins do. They also reduce coughing, cause constipation and euphoria, and most (but not all) can become addictive. It is the non-addictive possibilities that are currently being explored, along with generic and dose testing and the search for a "me too" drug. These drugs commonly cause vomiting when given in high doses, so that's a strong possibility on a drug study for narcotics.

Nonsteroidal anti-inflammatory drugs (NSAIDs)

These are all the rage these days as companies milk the pain vein with more headache pills. These drugs do not produce euphoria and are not addictive. They are also not particularly good at stopping pain *per se*, even though they do have some analgesic properties. What these drugs do is reduce inflammation and thereby reduce pain. Ibuprofen is a common NSAID which is now available OTC, but there are other, more potent, formulations out there. Tests involving these drugs are likely to be new versions, i.e., time-release formulas or tolerance tests. They can irritate the stomach and, in high doses, damage kidneys. Aspirin, too, it should be noted, is an NSAID and many studies involve examining new ways to deliver it without hurting the stomach (enteric coatings for instance). Because these drugs offer a direct and more physiological way to relieve pain than by acting on the central nervous system, there should be lots of tests for them for relief from everything from migraines to sunburn.

Other

There are other drugs that might loosely be termed "pain relievers," even though they do not do this directly. There are drugs to constrict blood vessels in an attempt to stop migraine headaches, there are drugs which are designed specifically to relieve the pain of gout, drugs for rheumatism, etc. All of these compounds may be used in a mixture with other drugs such as antihistamines.

Psychotropic Drugs

Here we go. The subject is vast. Under this classification I'm including drugs from sleeping pills to anti-psychotic medications. These tests can be particularly interesting since some of these compounds are designed to have profound effects on what are essentially subtle areas of the brain.

Benzodiazepines

Lately a class of drugs known as *benzodiazepines* have taken over the market for use as anxiolitics (anti-anxiety), hypnotics (sleeping pills), anticonvulsants and muscle relaxants. These drugs, while acting on the central nervous system, appear to affect more remote areas of the brain such as the limbic system and reticular formation.

The most famous benzodiazepine is Valium (diazepam) and has spawned a host of variations on the same theme. Depression, anxiety, panic disorders, sleeping problems, etc. are sexy diseases these days and drug companies are going full-speed ahead to develop their versions of various cures. They are also trying to find concoctions that will zero in on one condition only, without any side effects. Also important is the search for drugs that work more directly, without requiring metabolization in the liver. If you become involved with a study of these drugs you can expect a pretty mellow time of it, especially if you're being tested intravenously.

There are other anti-anxiety agents such as hydroxyzine, meprobamate, doxepin, or chlormezanone. Some of these drugs may be under investigation for other uses such as anti-emetics (anti-nausea) or even high blood pressure.

Anorectics

Ever since amphetamines went Schedule II (which makes them more difficult to prescribe) the hunt has been on for something just as good for weight loss. So far, at least a half dozen drugs that inhibit appetite have been developed. Many are simply analogs of amphetamines and, predictably, have some of the same effects: increased energy, wakefulness, tension, etc., etc. Fluoxetine (Prozac), too, seems to have promise as a weight-loss medication. As you can imagine, overweight America is clamoring for a pill to take those unsightly pounds off without the discomfort associated with dieting. You could easily be involved in a Phase One test of these types of drugs.

Anti-depressants

Here we have four basic classifications: Tricyclics, "fourth generation" tricyclics, Monoamine Oxidase Inhibitors (MAOIs) and a new class represented, so far, only by fluoxetine (Prozac). However, at the time of this writing, Smith-Kline-Beecham is already being slapped around by the FDA for prematurely marketing its "me too" version of Prozac called paroxetine, and Pfizer has announced its version, sertraline (to be marketed under the name Zoloft). All of these drugs are effective in relieving depression and other mental disorders, but not all of the time. Their specific actions are not known or fully understood but plenty of testing is going on with these compounds for use in treating bulimia, anorexia, obesity, obsessive-compulsive disorders, sexual dysfunction, narcolepsy, and a wide variety of mental/brain disorders.

Nootropics

One classification of drugs you may easily run into are what are known as *nootropics*. These are memory and intelligence enhancing drugs already in widespread use in Europe, none of which have been approved for us in the U.S. They will probably be used initially as treatment for Alzheimer's and senility, but have shown promise in other areas. Since these drugs have so far proven to be low in toxicity, experiments to determine their effects and especially their effects in combination with other drugs are likely, since it has been suggested that nootropic drugs have synergistic qualities when mixed.

In addition there are lots of anti-psychotic medications, all of which are useful in treating or at least controlling the symptoms of psychosis. Some of them can be quite powerful — a sane person would be transformed into a zombie if he took some of these at their therapeutic doses. Some of them can have bizarre side effects such as hallucinations, which some may find interesting while others may find uncomfortable.

Their exact mode of action is also generally unknown but they may be tested for possible exploitation of their side effects. As an example, Compazine (prochlorperazine), originally developed to control schizophrenia, is now used almost exclusively for its anti-emetic effect, which can be quite powerful even at low doses. There are other medications derived from ergot (a fungus which produces more than a few drugs, including LSD) and barbiturates, all of which can be used to treat mental conditions. The possibilities are endless, as are the variations on these drugs. In Phase One tests involving these types of medications, you may expect either low doses or entirely new classes of drugs. Be very wary of any test which requires you to take large doses of either barbiturates or anti-psychotics such as haloperidol or thorazine (see Chapter 5 on Renegade Studies).

Hormones

Among the most common hormones used in medicine are the estrogens, normally produced in large quantities by menstruating females. Estrogens, along with other hormones called progestins, are used in birth control pills. Besides these uses, both are useful in treating cancer. Lately there has been a lot of research into estrogen replacement for post-menopausal women, but hormones as a class of chemicals present almost endless possibilities for new drugs.

Hormones exert powerful influences over cell growth and health — all of the anabolic steroids that so dramatically increase muscle bulk and strength are hormones, for instance. Experiments with hormones should be common as drug companies explore their use to treat viruses (especially AIDS), reverse senility, heal wounds and treat cancer. Further, despite all the public hand-wringing about the ethics of it all, there will be investigation into using hormones to "sculpt" human beings, changing both physical and mental characteristics. Vasopressin, a posterior pituitary hormone, is currently used to treat some aspects of diabetes, but it has also been shown to increase mental capacity — something becoming more and more stylish in the medical community.

Researchers are likely to experiment with nasal sprays as a method of delivering hormones, but just because you get a spray at some test, that doesn't mean it's a hormone — nasal sprays may be the delivery system of the future because of the quick absorption obtained through the membranes in the nose.

Various types of "abortion pills" like RU-486 are also based on hormones and are also likely to be developed in the future.

Antibiotics

Penicillin hardly kills anything anymore, and a lot of people are allergic to it. So, over the years, drug companies have developed new and "stronger" antibiotics. It is a constant war, since all those bugs eventually develop resistances to whatever antibiotics we come up with. For awhile the bugs seemed to be winning and many patients with infections could no longer be treated with normal doses of oral antibiotics. People were getting hospitalized so that huge doses of drugs could be administered intravenously. But just lately some new antibiotics known as fluroquinolones have been discovered that are strong enough to kill off super infections and yet can be taken in pill form. Scientists know the war isn't over, however, and work will continue in this area. Surprisingly, some of the newer antibiotics don't seem to have the same problems with allergic reactions that earlier ones had, but they sometimes do affect the central nervous system causing, among other things, seizures.

Heart Medications

This is almost guaranteed to be a continuing boom. Sixty million people suffer from high blood pressure, millions more have coronary-vascular problems and plain old heart failures. Docs are doing bypasses all over the place but it isn't enough. Worse, the earliest and cheapest drugs (called beta blockers) used to slow down the heart and lower blood pressure had very unpleasant side effects such as tiredness and impotence. Small wonder you saw all those public service commercials exhorting men to take their medication!

Diuretics, too, still are being used to lower blood pressure, because they are dirt cheap. But these increase fat levels in the blood and deplete the body of potassium, which in turn can cause heart arythmia (erratic heartbeat), which will drive you to take antiarrythmics, which have lately been implicated in a lot of deaths. Antiarrythmics aren't in vogue these days because it seems they might be killing a lot more patients than they save.

Obviously there is a strong need and large demand for better drugs in this area.

So far the drug gurus have given us what are known as ACE inhibitors, which enlarge the blood vessels and inhibit water retention (as opposed to flushing it out like diuretics), and preserve kidney function. Ahhhh, that's more like it. And you can still get it up. But not everybody can take them.

So studies are being done on angiotension II blockers, which seem just as good as the ACE inhibitors. These drugs have already undergone most of their testing and should be available soon. Look for the "me too" rush on these. In fact, look for lots of anti-hypertensive (anti-high-blood-pressure) compounds.

Along with this there should be plenty of research into what are known as antihyperlipidemic agents — drugs that lower cholesterol. Since this is a very new field, it's difficult to speculate on just what is being tested. Expect anything. With the exception of a couple of products, anti-cholesterol drugs are unpleasant to take (one is a granulated, sandy product you have to gag down in a glass of water). They don't work too well and also have unpleasant side effects such as nausea. There may be "me too" studies out there. There may be stuff impossible to imagine. Mevacor (an anti-cholesterol), after all, came from some funky microbe dug up in Spain.

5

Renegade Studies

Occasionally you'll run across what amount to under-ground Phase One studies. These need not be avoided but should be approached with caution. You'll probably hear of them from other guinea pigs, or maybe you'll be approached by doctors or other researchers while nosing around for a normal study to take part in. Researchers are not always able to get permission for their experiments from their respective universities or hospitals. Nor from the Institutional Review Boards (IRBs) whose healthy consulting fees are on the line if they go too far in giving the OK to what poses too extreme or bizarre a risk to the patient.

Experiments you may run into include inquiries into sensory deprivation, cryogenics (the freezing of tissue, including whole bodies) or other experiments with suspended animation. A lot of heavy-duty psychological experimentation is going on out there involving research into past life regression, an approach to time travel that involves a person's being put into a hypnotic state. The movie *Flatliners* suggests at least some people have at least thought about experimenting with resurrection from death.

Obviously, all of these areas of research pose ethical and legal problems that might be best ignored from the point of view of the researchers.

Unfortunately, some of the people who get mixed up in these experiments are unwitting dupes or people in desperate situations. This is not to say you should not entertain the idea of participating in an experiment wherein you are deep-frozen and then brought back to life a few hours/days/whatevers later — there is a lot of exciting research being done in unorthodox areas. You *must* be aware of the danger and since there is no kindly IRB to look after its own ass as well as yours, you must be equipped to deal with these situations.

Try to determine the "legitimacy" of the researcher you're dealing with. Is he affiliated with a learning institute? Does he have a degree from some place you've heard of? Does he demonstrate any particular knowledge or do you have any particular knowledge that you can judge him by? Make sure there are no inconsistencies in what he tells you. If there is the slightest doubt in your mind about the experiment, even if it's a superstitious gut feeling — *do not do the experiment.*

Other danger signs include the feeling that you're being pressured into participating. Any scent of a con job telling you to hurry up and agree should set off the warning bells.

One of the loudest warning bells should go off if the researcher requires you to pay for anything. You should not have to foot any part of the bill at all, not for pre-experiment tests, not for drugs, accommodations... not for anything.

Do not listen only to the guy giving you the pitch to become a guinea pig for this research. Check with your own doctor or an independent doctor about his/her thoughts on the experiment. Ask to see the informed consent form. Never sign anything that would waive any of your rights if you should be harmed during the experiment. Once again, although the FDA does not require it, compassionate human beings won't ask you to accept all the risk and the prudent guinea pig won't give up his rights. Of course, in a renegade experiment, FDA rules are not often observed.

What kind of pay arrangements are there? Do they sound adequate and feasible? See if any of the money is paid to you up front. In general, use your instinct and don't be lured by money or anything else into something too dangerous.

Of course, one man's danger is another man's adventure, so this is subjective. I met a guinea pig who participated in an experiment in which he was secluded in a sensory deprivation tank, dosed with sedatives and exposed to sub-audible tapes of people arguing, shouting, and other disconcerting sounds for days at a time. The point of the experiment was to explore what sort of effects outside influences might have on a fetus. The experience had a profound effect on him. He would burst out crying for no reason; he sometimes felt he was losing his mind. In this case he was almost constantly surrounded by psychiatric personnel whom he trusted. In the end he volunteered for another week of the treatment.

Sometimes you may be facing a Phase Two or Three study in which the main benefit is relief from a disease you are currently suffering from. As this book deals only with Phase One tests (those on healthy human beings), I cannot adequately address these types of studies except to say the situation is ripe for quackery and rip-offs. This is where desperate people can fall prey to assholes who claim they have discovered new ways to relieve arthritis, paralysis, blindness, the heartbreak of psoriasis, or damn near anything else.

One of the clearest signs of a liar is someone who asks you for money. In no case does a legitimate FDA-approved test (whether Phase One, Two, Three, or Four) ask you to pay for anything. Please be skeptical. If it sounds too good to be true, everyone knows it probably is. Also be wary of researchers who try to persuade you with the results of a single study, or pull out a newspaper article to buttress their claims. By the time something shows up in the newspaper, it is old news or else a hoax. This is not the way true scientific inquiry is conducted. "Miracle" cures are just that — miracles. They can happen, but don't count on it. If you have any persistent doubts, you would be well advised to contact the nearest FDA office listed in your phone book, since Phase Two and Three studies almost never pay anything anyway.

On the other hand, if you come across a legit Phase Two or Three study, give it some serious thought. There are plenty of them out there and you are likely to get excellent care, the most advanced treatment possible under the direction of experts. It will also be free and, more importantly, it will remain free even after the test is over if you are experiencing benefits. If you are involved in a study that pits a particular drug against a placebo and results show that the drug clearly is better than the placebo, the tests will be stopped, you will be informed as to what's going on and given the opportunity to get the real drug. Nobody is allowed to suffer needlessly just to prove that a drug works.

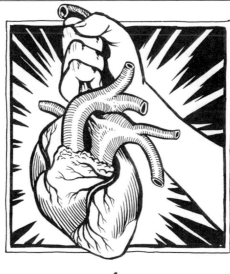

1

Our Bodies, Our Bank Accounts

The Need for Organs

Every year a couple thousand people die while awaiting organ transplants they are scheduled to get, but, for some reason, don't happen in time. This occurs after waiting for years in misery and vain hope. Another 20,000 or so people could use an organ transplant but are resigned to living with a diseased organ. A large number of these people are in need of kidneys. Without them they must spend several hours a day, a few days per week, hooked up to a dialysis machine to clean their blood. The rest of the time they watch their fluid intake and try to stay near a dialysis center. It is costly, more than $25,000 per year.

Surgeons perform some 8,000 to 9,000 kidney transplants annually with a 93% success rate. There is supposedly an elaborate nationwide (in fact, world-wide) network set up to co-ordinate organ donation between those in need and those who have just died. Unfortunately, it doesn't work very well. There is great difficulty in obtaining enough organs when you're dependent on people who have died and left behind healthy, intact bodies within a few hours of a hospital. Traffic accidents provide most organs for transplant.

Invented in the early 1950's, kidney transplantation has progressed to the point that it is a virtual cure for kidney disease. New drugs to prevent rejection and better understanding of matching techniques make the operation a veritable breeze.

Still, the estimated 18,000 people who desperately need a kidney continue to suffer not only a diminished quality of life but a shortening of their lives while waiting for a kidney that probably will not come. There are thousands more who will die unless they get a bone marrow transplant. And still thousands more who could benefit from liver, pancreas and lung transplants die because of the difficulty of locating suitable donors, one of whose qualifications, unfortunately, is that they must be dead. Corpses are essentially the only source of organs in the United States today. There are also many people who, being poor candidates for any transplant because of their particularly bad health or age, are not considered "qualified" to even be on the waiting list. The longer you wait, the greater your chances that you will cross a certain threshold of sickness and become too sick to be healed.

At the same time all this is going on, there are millions of people walking around with two healthy kidneys, nice big livers and bone marrow a-plenty that they could give to these people and dramatically transform their lives. There is even a small part of the population (less than 1%) that is born with three functioning kidneys! Who could better afford to give up a kidney?

Why There Are So Few Kidneys, Hearts, Etc.

Donations are rare, they depend on altruism, often at a time when a family is confronted with the sudden death of a loved one. Organ removal and transplantation paints a grisly picture in one's mind that is difficult to come to grips with even for those who are not grief-stricken. It also affirms in an indisputable way that the loved one is dead. Removing a person's organs is not the way to bring someone back to life.

Currently American "ethics" has declared organ and tissue selling to be illegal on some vague, not even religion-based notion that there is something suspect and wrong with live, non-related donors giving up organs. Not even for free.

So we wait for people to die.

And that should be enough. After all, every year 2.2 million people die in the United States, of which as many as 25,000 fit the stringent classifications necessary to be an organ donor. These people must be, in effect, perfectly healthy but for the fact that they are brain dead — and even then for only a few hours. Yet fewer than 4,000 of these potential donors are actually used for organ transplants. Even more appalling is the lack of transplantable tissues (such as skin, bones, joints, corneas) that could be harvested from lower quality cadavers that end up in cemeteries or cremated. The requirements for tissue donation are less stringent and make the potential donor group far larger — perhaps hundreds of thousands. Yet surgeons can only get their hands on the remains of some 45,000 of these cadavers.

Meanwhile burn patients continue to suffer, blind people stay sightless, deaf people live in silence and people have limbs amputated needlessly. These are people who could benefit from tissues belonging to dead people, who obviously have little use for them any more. And people suffer and die while waiting for organs they will never get, while researchers dream up faulty mechanical versions of complex internal organs. Remember the artificial heart and how great that worked?

To add even more urgency to the issue, surgical methods are constantly being developed and perfected to cure fatal conditions by transplanting organs from living donors without compromising the health of the donor. This is especially true for liver transplants, as surgeons find they can remove small slices of a healthy liver for transplantation into a diseased body — where the healthy slice soon regenerates and saves the life of the victim. This only requires a small piece of liver from a living donor. The donor must be a pretty good genetic match, usually a family member is best suited, but there are always others out there who happen to match as well. Unfortunately, these people must be dead before their livers can be used.

This situation should be particularly distressing to minorities, whose genetic make up virtually assures the impossibility of finding an appropriate donor. For black people the problem is especially bad. While about 80% of blacks can accept organs from almost anyone, the rest need organs donated by other blacks. Yet black people are among the least likely to donate either organs or blood. In addition, blacks are proportionately in far greater need of kidney transplants — about one third of all patients on dialysis are black. The chances of a black person getting a suitable transplant, whether for a kidney or any other organ, are low. Other minorities — Jews, Orientals, American Indians — face similar problems.

Surgeons are reluctant to use living donors in any case, even if they are family members. Even those whose job it is to cajole organs from a dead person's family are reluctant to use "hard sell" tactics in their jobs. No law compels a person to donate any part of their body and almost all hospitals and doctors refuse to use unrelated donors for organ transplants. As I said, they even have qualms about using a family member as a source for an organ. In medical journals doctors publish hand-wringing essays about "pressuring" suitable family members into donating an organ to save a sibling or a parent's life but there is no reason to believe the public itself sees any problem. Indeed some desperate people have been forced to conceive children specifically for use as organ donors, since no matches can be found within the family — although there are non-relatives out there with suitable tissues.

Not that people are lining up to donate their organs to perfect strangers. They're not. Most people don't even sign papers allowing their organs to be used after they're dead. And the sale of organs or tissues is illegal in the United States, since both state and federal laws make it a felony to knowingly purchase or sell for any type of valuable consideration organs or tissues for transplantation.

Predictably enough, the same laws which make it jail-time for anyone who'd try to make a buck off a dead man's heart make it absolutely permissible for all persons involved in any legal transplant operation to get paid. That includes everybody from the guy who carts a kidney in a cooler to the hospital, to the kindly hospital chaplain who cajoles families to let their just-dead kin be parted out for the good of strangers — and the profit of the hospital that employs him. The *only* people excluded from payment are the donor himself and/or his family members. Their sole remuneration is a warm feeling of charity — presumably even toward the surgeon who performs the kidney operation for a $25,000 to $30,000 fee.

Who Owns You?

The central problem of organ donation is ownership. Legislators and judges have skirted around this thing even while they implicitly recognize that an organ is, at some point, property and that somebody owns it. The wholesome Red Cross has even toyed with a policy of increasing the price it charges for blood (obtained for free from charity-minded citizens) to hospitals which do not donate tissues to its newly formed tissue banks. Blood banks, including the Red Cross, buy and sell blood to each other all the time, and end up charging customers as much as $120 per pint of blood that was handed over to them out of pure altruism. Money is made on donated blood at every step of the process except for the person who supplies it in the first place. And the profit is hefty. Between 1980 and 1988 the Red Cross made more than $300 million by selling donated blood.

The same sort of thing goes on with body parts. Organ procurement organizations set up cozy arrangements with favored tissue banks, notifying them that they've got a good body on hand just as soon as they've removed all saleable organs. The situation has made it so that many organ transplants are done on an informal basis. Hospitals tend to hold onto any brain-dead people they get for use in organ transplants at that particular hospital. Similarly, scientists looking for organs for use in their research use what have been described as "back door" methods to obtain organs and tissue from patients about to undergo surgery or from unclaimed bodies at the city morgue. Even diseased tissue is valuable to researchers.

Theoretically, everybody's in constant contact throughout the world so that if a kidney becomes available in West Germany, a dying little girl in Podunk, Arkansas will have a crack at it and the organ will be jetted to her right away. In practice this is rare and if you want an organ, you'd best sign up at a big hospital in a big city and hope for icy streets. You should also try to be white and of a common blood type, etc.

If a person's body were to be used for only its heart, lungs, liver, kidneys and pancreas (as he agrees to do when he signs up for donor registration on his drivers license) he helps generate more than a million dollars in medical business. More money is made if anybody gets ahold of his jawbone, corneas, ligaments or other valuable tissues. Clearly we're talking about a commodity here. A person's body is his property. At the very *least*, it is his property.

This fact was made starkly evident in 1989 when surgeons at the University of California removed the cancerous spleen of one John Moore. The doctors then used cells from Moore's one-of-a-kind spleen to produce interferon and other pharmaceuticals which netted them millions of dollars. Moore sued, saying he should be compensated for his role in the production of these profitable items. His surgeons disagreed, saying they were essentially making use of material Moore clearly didn't want any longer.

The California Supreme Court gave an inconclusive ruling, finding "several reasons to doubt" that Moore retained any property interest in his spleen once it was removed, but on the other hand finding that his physicians should have informed him that they planned to make a little spending money on Moore's spleen once they'd taken it out.

So, at least in California, your body belongs to you, but only while you have physical possession of it. That being the case, the time to think about what can be done with your body is now, not after somebody starts carving it up.

The whole prohibition on selling body parts is based on the squeamish fear our culture has about our innards in general. The thought of a loved one being parted out for other people is repulsive for grieving relatives (who are still consulted by the kindly chaplain even when a donor card has been signed). Often, permission to use a freshly dead body, which is useful for no more than about 15 hours after death, is denied by the family on the grounds that the deceased "has been through enough." There is no incentive for anyone to either sign a donor card ahead of time or to give permission for their relative to be used for organ donation other than pure altruism — which has so far proven inadequate.

The perception of ghoulishness of organ donation is strengthened in the public's mind by stories of people receiving bills for the removal of their loved one's organs (yes, this has happened), further deepening the pain and encouraging people to get the whole thing over with by denying the corpse to surgeons.

The need for organs has also spawned a series of stories, most of which are untrue, about people being kidnapped and deprived of organs, of street children in foreign countries being carved up and sold to wealthy people.

Past Experience

This is all reminiscent of Britain's problem with grave-robbing in the early 1800's. At that time the only corpses that were allowed to be dissected were the bodies of executed people. Crowds would clamor around the hanged man, desperately fighting over him for sale to doctors who needed bodies to practice surgery and teach anatomy. But there simply weren't enough executed people to go around, so doctors were forced to buy bodies on the black market.

The result was not only widespread graverobbing but an increase in the murders of the elderly and vulnerable — since the freshest corpses brought the highest prices.

A certain Scotsman named W. Burke was eventually executed (and of course, dissected) in 1820 after being convicted of murdering a string of young girls and old women for sale to doctors. What is most interesting about this is that these killers who stalked people to sell to doctors were not murdering in order to satisfy some blood-lust or to finance an illicit drug habit — they were murdering for the bodies themselves!

Graverobbing as well as murdering for corpses came to a halt in 1832 when the state finally allowed the bodies of dead paupers to be used by doctors in their research. It seems entirely possible that all the crimes committed today because of the dearth of body parts would similarly disappear if organ sales were decriminalized. This includes the crime of allowing people to die for lack of readily available organs and tissues. This is a very unfortunate situation, especially since most people see the wisdom of voluntary organ sales. A recent CNN/Time Magazine poll showed that while only 6% of respondents favored forcing a person to donate an organ, 56% would be prepared to buy one if necessary. Nearly one fourth would be willing to conceive a child merely for the purpose of providing life-saving tissue.

The Body Business

For the sake of argument, this book will assume that all parts of a person's body are his property and that he can do with them as he pleases, including transfer ownership upon his death just like he can any other property. However, it must be stressed that any sales of organs in the United States are illegal and if you make deals with your organs, you'll have to conduct the whole business under the table. This should be no big problem — people conduct illegal business all the time. It's just that you can't make up a contract and go wave it around in court. Nevertheless, it's a good idea to write up some sort of agreement whenever you're engaged in a business deal. May we suggest that the actual nature of the deal get disguised in the verbiage of the contract? A decent lawyer should be able to help you out here.

The sale of organs is, however, not illegal in plenty of other places in the world. It's not illegal in Britain or Germany, for instance (although this may change soon), and it's not illegal in India, where kidney and skin sales are common (but prices are on the low side). It is also not illegal in many southeast Asian countries. Filipino prisoners serving long sentences make money to support their families by selling their kidneys for practically nothing to wealthy Japanese. In India, kidney-selling has become almost a cottage industry, with the relatively large payments serving as capital for impoverished peasants.

In my opinion the sale of organs should be permitted. The argument that this will only encourage the rich to exploit the poor is weak. The rich always exploit the poor. And in the matter of organ transplants it is the rich who end up with the organs anyway, by virtue of their good health insurance plans, connections, and ability to pay for a real search for a suitable donor. On the contrary, organ sales would allow people to fully exploit their own property for whatever use they see fit. It would quickly increase the number of transplantable organs and encourage more organ transplants. The price of a transplant may even come down. The price of immunosuppressive drugs for those receiving transplants would come down. Further, 18,000 dialysis patients can stop laying down $25,000 per year, get off the machines, and start leading normal lives.

Prisoners, who might otherwise have nothing to contribute to society, could either give their organs away or sell them to help support their families, as is done in the Philippines. It is one of the more bizarre aspects of our society that the law does not permit organs from executed prisoners to be used in transplants. In some cases the law is moot, since the method of execution (electrocution, for instance) destroys the organs for that purpose anyway.

Any way you look at it, it seems wrong to waste a resource that could truly benefit people in need, out of some superstitious fear of our own bodies.

But it is not the purpose of this book to argue the case for legalization of organ sales. For the moment, it is against the law, but it need not always be.

What Your Body Is Good For

There are two times when you can sell parts of your body, while you're still alive and after you're dead. Chapter 2 covers those parts of your body you can sell now, and Chapter 3 covers those parts you can sell after you're dead. Obviously if you want to profit from, say, your heart, you'll have to get the recipient to agree to take delivery later on, at an unspecified date. This seems unlikely. Once laws preventing the sale of organs are repealed and property rights are recognized, there will undoubtedly spring up a number of clearinghouses that will sign up organ "vendors" and either arrange for partial or full payment up front, or perhaps pay out to the next of kin. In this way, it would be possible for you to will the proceeds of your body to your heirs.

Until then, there are parts of your body you can cut out, and stay alive.

2

While You're Alive

Kidneys

You've got two kidneys and you only need one of them to clean your blood. The other is back-up. Nature gave you two of them for a good reason: you'll die pretty quickly without them. But normally you will not lose or damage either of them. People who have lost the functions of both their kidneys would die were it not for the invention of the dialysis machine — a device which mechanically extracts the blood from a patient's body and cleans it. It is not particularly pleasant but it is the only alternative to a kidney transplant. So far no one has come up with an artificial kidney and there aren't any on the foreseeable horizon. Luckily, kidney transplants are an excellent way to treat people with end-stage kidney disease. Currently only about 14 percent of those receiving a kidney get one from a relative. The rest get one from a cadaver. Everybody else waits. There is a market.

Your risk of dying by donating a kidney is about one in 5,000. It definitely hurts, sometimes more than it does the person receiving it. Sometimes the disparity in pain and the fact that the recipient of the kidney gets so much more attention has caused feelings of resentment and depression in family members who have donated kidneys. This problem is less likely to happen to you. But it should be noted that all organ donors experience a degree of empathy for the people who get their organs and often become depressed should the operation be unsuccessful. Some have even become suicidal. Once again this involves family members and all the attendant emotional circumstances. For those conducting a business transaction, this should not be such a great problem. The operation will cause some pain, leave about an eight-inch scar and keep you hospitalized for about a week. But you should count on a good two months to heal.

One of the greatest worries for a kidney donor is that he is exposing himself to the threat of finding himself in the same position someday should something go wrong with his remaining kidney. There is no evidence to support this fear. One kidney is more than sufficient for a single body.

Bone Marrow

Marrow is one of the few body products actively solicited by procurement agencies, but they still won't offer you money for it. There is a registry of people who are willing to donate, as well as a waiting list of people who need it, although you can't get your hands on the second list at all. Bone marrow can be used to cure leukemia or Hodgkin's disease. The numbers are sobering: half of the patients who get fresh, healthy marrow survive, but the odds of a match from the general population are one in 20,000. Every day, 25 people die who could have used a marrow transplant.

The risk to the donor is obviously less than for the recipient, but there is still some risk. The National Marrow Donor Program studied some 3,000 donors from 1969 through 1984 and found that 10 of them suffered problems like irregular heartbeats or abnormal breathing. Because many surgeons require the operation of extracting marrow to be performed under general anesthesia (it is possible to have only a spinal block but the person must remain absolutely still during the 1-3 hour operation) there is always the small risk of dying on the operating table.

The operation itself consists of having a syringe inserted into the back of the pelvic bone just above the buttocks. Then about a cup of the thick red fluid is sucked out and given to the recipient intravenously. For the recipient the operation is a picnic. For you, it hurts. After recovering from the general anesthesia, you're going to endure a week and a half of lower back pain that one patient described as similar to "being butted in the back with a football helmet."

One note should be made here. Once you've committed yourself to selling someone your marrow, *do not* back out on the deal. In order to prepare for this operation, the recipient will have undergone a week's worth of intensive radiation therapy to totally destroy his own marrow cells and make it easier for the new ones to take root. If you back out, the patient will die within a week.

Since the odds of a match are so long, it might be a good idea if a new registry were started by those willing to sell their marrow. These people would be more reliable donors since the profit motive would induce them to drop whatever they're doing and come to the aid of a stranger when called — even if it is years after they've signed up. Currently this is posing something of a problem for the non-profit folks.

Liver

A healthy person can lose three quarters of his liver and survive. A few weeks later the organ will have completely regenerated itself. Thus a liver is theoretically an ideal organ for transplantation but there are still problems with the procedure. First, the liver is difficult to operate on. It is full of blood and very fragile. But it is possible to cut part of it away and transplant it into another person. This operation was first done at the University of Chicago in 1989 when a mother donated a part of her liver to her daughter who had suffered congenital liver failure. The operation took 14 hours and required three follow-up operations for the daughter to deal with bleeding. The mother suffered no post-operative problems.

For you, the operation hurts. Livers simply cannot be manipulated without causing painful bruising. There is also a not-so-small risk of dying during the operation. Serious and unstoppable bleeding kills one in every one hundred patients undergoing this procedure. You might want to keep this in mind while setting your price, or even deciding whether it's worth it. Remember, the other person has about a 100% chance of dying if they don't get a liver.

Since livers are so important and cannot currently be replaced by any machine, transplantation is necessary to save lives. If the procedure can be made safer and perhaps easier, and if more livers were available, there could come a day when liver transplants could be used to treat people with liver ailments long before they end up half dead in the hospital.

Since a liver can regenerate itself, there exists the possibility of donating a slice of your liver on a regular basis. Liver farming could become a lucrative business for anyone inclined to take the risk.

Lungs

Lung transplants have been possible for some years now, often along with a heart. Obviously the latter come from cadavers. But within the last few years, doctors have begun trying to transplant the lobes of a living donor's lungs instead of the entire organ. So far, few of these operations have been conducted and their success rate is unclear.

Corneas

Corneas are harvested from dead people in the United States, but are for sale from living donors overseas. In this operation, the lens of an eye is removed and implanted into an eye which has been blinded by cataracts. This is really virgin territory here in the States. Since the system is already in place and since eyes "keep" pretty well, there is not the urgency involved in harvesting.

Nevertheless, the latest information I have is that the price of a cornea in India is somewhere around $4,000 dollars. Don't start ruining things by lowering the price. If an impoverished Indian peasant can get four grand, price your eye accordingly. And, yes, you will be disfigured by the operation and probably have to wear an eye patch or get a glass eye and you will lose your depth perception as well as disqualify yourself for certain types of jobs and licenses, etc.

The Costs Involved

There are numerous costs involved with becoming a donor, mainly in the initial screening process to determine whether your tissue is suitable. These tests are sometimes paid for by charity groups seeking to promote tissue donation and they are sometimes paid for by the potential recipient. In any case, you should not have to incur this expense, and if you do, you should charge it back to the customer.

Depending on the kind of deal you hammer out with the customer, you should have all expenses taken care of. However, you can't expect them to agree to anything extravagant. Only haggling will determine what's extravagant or not. Just be prepared to deal — besides, you hold a lot of the good cards before the operation takes place. Afterwards, when they've got the organ, they may not feel so magnanimous. And a lawsuit to have a kidney returned to you seems a time-wasting way at best to remedy what you perceive as a bad deal.

The risk of death for donors as a whole (whether donating kidneys, liver slices or whatever) appears to be about one in 5,000. For some operations it is much higher, for others it is much lower. All of them involve considerable pain and scarring. Removing a lobe of just one lung will leave you with an 18-inch scar that runs from your chest to your back, and it will be extremely painful. The pain may even be long-lasting enough to disturb you for a year or so. Always check with an independent doctor about the ramifications of becoming a living donor. Having an organ removed can even cause psychological problems associated with loss.

How Much To Charge

Here is a truly vexing question, since the field is so new. In India, the going rate for a kidney is about $1,500, while Filipino prisoners selling their kidneys to Japanese patients get about half that. In Egypt, the price is more like $10,000, in a fairly brisk market. But you have to remember that fifteen hundred is a lot of money to an Indian man who might otherwise not save that kind of money in his lifetime. It is also worth noting that the price of a kidney has dropped in the last few years as Indians vie with one another to sell their kidneys. The price of a kidney can fluctuate, too, as supply and demand wax and wane. It may also be that you can tout your kidney as superior to another man's. Living a clean life, having good genes, being healthy — all these things can increase the worth of your kidney.

In China, an operation to receive the kidney of an executed prisoner, including a few weeks of hospitalization and medications, runs about $10,000. Most transplants are done at the Nan Fang and the Zhongshan hospitals in the province of Canton about 80 miles north of Hong Kong. But Chinese transplants pose problems. Many crucial tests, such as hepatitis B surface antigen, antibody to human group, other common tissue compatibility tests and even basic blood typing are not always done, so the rejection rate is high. This is especially so if the patient fails to obtain proper post-operative care such as the administration of anti-rejection drugs. Also, these junkets tend to be run out of Hong Kong, which officially disapproves of the trade and refuses to provide vital cyclosporin to anyone coming back from China with a new kidney. Your potential customer may say they can get a better price in China or India, but this is by no means sure.

One angle that may be of help to an American who needs a kidney is to trade on your American citizenship. Chinese people from Hong Kong are eagerly paying $50,000 and $100,000 to get visas to the U.S. to escape Hong Kong's integration into mainland China in 1997. Why not work out some sort of an agreement whereby you marry, adopt or otherwise sponsor some Chinese person if he or someone in his family gives up a kidney and pays all the expenses? This angle can be used in a number of places where life is horrible — even in the United States. You might even consider trading your kidney for a permanent residency in Europe, for instance.

In Egypt, there are six major kidney transplant centers performing about one kidney transplant per day from live donors. Many of the customers are rich Libyans who also promise jobs in Libya when the operation is over. Some come through and others don't. Once a guy has got your kidney don't expect to have any more dealings with him.

The price for a cornea in India is currently around $4,000. Giving up an eye is a lot to ask of someone, after all, and staying blind is a lot to endure. How much should you charge for your eye? Consider that you will lose your depth perception and one of your eyes will become disfigured. Cornea replacement for the donor eye is always a possibility, but sort of defeats the purpose. If an Indian peasant can get four thousand, you have a rough guide for setting the price of your cornea already.

A hunk of skin (used for skin grafts) goes for only around $50 in India. Skin is a little difficult to transplant and no single donor can give a sufficient amount to help any one person, so any appreciable skin sales business will have to go through a skin clearinghouse, much as it does today on a non-profit basis.

There are advertisements in Hong Kong newspapers for package deals that will fly a customer to India, perform the operation, and fly the customer home again for a set price. Similar deals exist in Europe although they are frowned upon. Many countries, such as England and Germany, are seeking to curb the practice. One Soviet firm offered round-trip airfare, hospitalization, and a new kidney to Germans for $68,570 — payable in hard currency. The German government stepped in to stop this particular deal but there are others operating, mainly out of India. Newspaper advertisements for kidneys are forbidden in Egypt, even though it's a center of the kidney trade.

In short, the market will determine the price according to availability, demand, and quality. You should consider also how much you want for your time, pain and effort. There are some people who wouldn't sell their kidney for a million dollars and others who'd gladly dump it for a couple of thousand.

Depending on your health, degree of desperation, and other factors, you might consider a price range of $20,000 to $50,000 or more for your kidney.

Organ Warehousing

It is possible to graft "extra" organs into a human body where they will live on as long as they have access to a blood supply. This raises the possibility of using your body as a storage area for organs you may purchase yourself and plan to re-sell in the future. In this way it is possible to buy, say, a kidney from a cheap source and then resell it for a better price. There are disadvantages to this, namely that you'll have to undergo an extra operation to put the organ into storage and it may not be worth the time, pain, and money. But it is possible.

Selling Is Better Than Donating

There is a lot of psychological baggage surrounding organ donations. People who receive an organ from a cadaver often wonder who the person was whose organs have given them a new chance at life. They may also feel guilt that it is somehow their fault that the person died and that they don't deserve the organ. Or they feel pressured to somehow live up to the gift. This problem is eliminated with organ sales, since the person isn't getting anything for free and you have agreed to sell under non-coercive circumstances. If for some reason, the recipient has not already met you (and that may happen if organ-brokering goes big time), they may want to meet you (and you may want to charge a fee for this).

On the donor's side of the issue there is also a great deal of guilt should the organ *not* thrive and save the patient. If the recipient is a family member, the donor may become quite depressed should anything go wrong. Suicide has occurred under these circumstances. Further, a surprising amount of resentment can grow between family members who donate/receive organs. Recipients feel they owe so much that they become bitter toward their benefactor, feeling that nothing they do can be enough to repay him. Donors become resentful of those whose lives they've helped save since most of the attention focuses on the recipient. He, too, may become bitter since, after all, it would have all been impossible without him.

This is exactly the situation that developed between a Miss America contestant and her brother. She had received one of his kidneys and their relationship soured to the point that they did not even speak to one another for 19 months. So, what would seem to be a great act of love and charity can cause real emotional hardship and damage when family members and/or friends are involved.

Obviously these are not problems when the organ transplant is a business transaction, although there may be other problems to deal with. People may accuse the organ-vendor of gouging or preying on the vulnerable. Organ-buyers may be seen as callous jerks who pay a pittance for a person's organ, who don't truly pay enough to the person who saves their life.

In short, the same negative feelings surrounding any other business deal will crop up in the organ business.

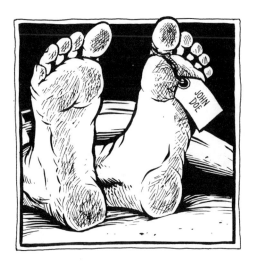

3

After You're Dead

Tissues From Corpses

A healthy donor's corpse can provide at least thirty kinds of tissues, some of which you can live without, some of which you can't really give until you are dead, and others of which (elbows, for instance) are not presently practical to sell while alive even though it is theoretically possible.

Among the most important parts of a body that are needed are:

- the heart, which can alternatively be parted out into four valves
- the lungs (or just the lobes if you're still alive)
- kidneys (two, if you're dead)
- pancreas
- 2 hip joints
- a jawbone

- 6 ear bones
- 2 corneas (one, if you're alive)
- limb bones and ribs
- ligaments, tendons and cartilage
- skin
- blood vessels

Bones are especially useful, since both bone and other connective tissues are "immunologically privileged," meaning the body won't reject them as it does other foreign bodies. Bone transplants don't require the suppression of the body's immune system and can be completely healed within one year.

Bone banking is likely to become a bigger business in the coming years, partly because it is not as regulated as some of the solid organ banks, such as for kidneys. Besides this, bone banking until about ten years ago was run as a part of the U.S. Navy. Today, hospitals set up their own small bone banks and compete with one another for business. A for-profit bone and tissue company, Allograft Inc., is already thriving in San Diego, where the organization procures, shapes, grinds, sterilizes and stores bones, bone paste, chips and other related products.

Many cities operate tissue banks to store these things, for future use. Items such as cartilage keep very well, as do corneas. Anybody trying to exploit their body's money-making potential should keep in mind that virtually every part of the body is of some use to someone.

Dealing With The Body Snatchers

Once a person looks like he's going to die and leave behind some pretty good organs, the body snatchers are quickly called in. Their first job is to get consent from family members to remove organs and tissues from the recently deceased loved one. It doesn't matter if that loved one signed a donor card, the law still allows surviving family members to revoke permission and they often do. Hospital personnel know this and have developed sophisticated techniques to cajole you into giving permission. Only certain people are allowed to approach you about the matter and there is a battery of representatives from various religions to help you decide to do the right thing.

At the same time they're making their case while your relative beeps away in a room full of machinery, they've probably also contacted organ recipients who may be on the way to the hospital at that moment. Time is of the essence. They may have only a few hours to get a heart or a pair of lungs. Now's the time to cut a deal.

Keep in mind that the hospital personnel are forbidden by law to offer you any sort of remuneration at all for your relative's organs. They can't even buy you dinner, although they might. Training materials for organ procurers suggest opening lines like this before getting down to the nitty gritty: "I know you've been here for a long time today, could I offer you something to drink?"

In fact, the training manuals emphasize the difficulty of the situation and go to great lengths to describe ways of dealing with bereaved, hysterical people about what is at best a touchy situation. So the whole thing is choreographed.

First, you and any other relatives will be removed from any general group and brought to a comfortable-looking room with sofa, table and chairs. The person or people responsible for talking to you will do anything to put you at ease. They probably won't sit directly across from you or touch you, as these things convey confrontation and power. They will speak softly, their body language will be very non-threatening. They are instructed to move slowly, to keep their arms down and palms open. They will sit with a slight backward tilt. They will frequently lower their gaze.

They may open the conversation with something like: "Our hospital routinely offers families the opportunity of organ/tissue donation at a time like this." Or some other phrase to make it sound like this is your idea. But they will not allow you to back away. One training manual suggests that the procurer "use concrete, metaphoric language" with the next of kin. "Be consistent," it advises, "DEAD — not clinically dead, essentially dead, or just brain dead."

You will have already been given the opportunity to see the loved one's body and will have heard how dead they are from the doctor. They will reinforce this.

"Go back over the medical situation with them to assess their understanding, overcome lingering denial, and fill in gaps in information," the training manual continues.

"Express sympathy over the situation."

Although there are many things they will tell you (that it won't cost you anything, how the body won't be disfigured, how much the transplant will benefit others, etc.) there is one thing they will not ask you and that's if you have ever thought about or discussed organ donation.

Even though they will consistently tell you that you *do not* have to donate (and you don't) they don't want to hear any talk about any prior consent problems.

This is your opening. Mention it. Bring up the subject that maybe your dear departed loved one once expressed horror at the thought of being parted out. Or that maybe he said he'd just read something that made him change his mind. Or perhaps there were certain organs he said he'd rather not donate. Or you just don't remember, maybe it was someone else who said that.

This will put them on alert that you are not an easy sell. But they won't give up. Hospital materials I have seen suggest reactions to "What if they say no," just like any good salesman should learn. One suggestion says, "if they're wishy-washy, check out reasons for being unsure, but don't push. Chances are they still have unanswered questions or concerns." It also reminds the procurer that it's OK to say *no* to organ transplants. They won't beg you. The last thing they need is to come off like an evil Dr. Frankenstein.

Brain Dead But Still Body Alive

If you are unfortunate enough to have a relative who is being kept alive mechanically, you will also be unfortunate enough to hear some of the "metaphoric" descriptions of how the person appears to be alive, but is not. Among those I have seen are:

To describe a corpse on a ventilator:

"It's true your daughter's heart is beating and she's warm, but that doesn't mean she is still in her body. The body is like a house. And the heart is like a furnace. A furnace can still be on, even when no one is at home any longer."

Worse imagery comes up if the body still possesses some reflex motions. Here are a couple of gems I've run across:

"You know how your muscles twitch as you relax and go to sleep. What you saw is a reflex motion. It's the body's way of relaxing into death." Or,

"It's like when someone dives off a diving board. The board continues to move after they've left it and are in the air. Jimmy is no longer in his body."

Or my favorite:

"If you've ever taken Carol swinging, you know how swings still move after children have jumped out of them. Carol's body is like an empty swing."

When they start talking like this you know they're serious.

How To Deal

One of the best things to do is simply give permission, obtain promises that you won't be billed for organ removal and that the body won't be mutilated and go home. Having a loved one die suddenly (as is often the case) is traumatic in the extreme. The thought of trying to make money off it should be sickening. On the other hand, people do buy cemetery plots before death and try to get a good deal. They just do it while they're still healthy. Once again, the time to think about organ vending is prior to death, not when you're grief-stricken. If you don't make plans for this kind of hard-nosed wheeling and dealing now, I urge you to forget it. Do not try to hammer out business deals over dead relatives in such an extreme situation. In this case, please donate or don't donate and be done with it. You've got far more important things to occupy your thoughts and emotions than money.

That having been said, let's look at a strategy for dealing.

The first thing you should try for is forgiveness of any outstanding hospital bills. The procurer may be in a good position to arrange this. Not only is this the easiest way to "buy" organs, since no money changes hands and any "losses" incurred by the hospital are smaller than whatever you owe them, this is highly possible. Besides, it may only be that you owe the hospital a few thousand or even a few hundred dollars.

This method has the added benefit of letting you avoid the pain later on when the bill comes. It's amazing, but for all their soppy death metaphors and "we understand what you're going through's" the hospital will be very stubborn about letting you off the hook for any amount of money. You've got to be just as stubborn.

I would suggest that you make it clear that they can have all the organs they want, *if they will let you go home and not bother you anymore.* Don't say anything about money directly. Tell them, yes, yes, you can have little Carol's heart, corneas, whatever — just don't compound my pain by billing me for anything. Stress that you don't want to be billed for *anything.* You just want to go home and begin grieving with your family and not have to think about this any longer.

If the conversation is taking place on the phone, tape record it. If it's in person, personalize it. Look straight into the procurer's eyes and make a deal. Call him or her by name, make it clear that you understand you will not be responsible for ANY costs concerning little Carol's empty swing. Not the ambulance ride, not the failed operation, not the complimentary drink they offered you. Present it as a matter of grief. You don't want to be bothered with this any more. You couldn't bear to go to the mailbox one day and see a staggering bill for Carol's empty swing. Suddenly you would be forced to think of her death and worse... her parting out.

This is a reasonable request. After all, the hospital is about to make perhaps a half million bucks off your loved one — all you want is not to have to pay for a failed operation, not to have to deal with this loss over a period of months while you struggle to pay off the debt. If it is at all possible, get some kind of promise in writing, even if it's something scribbled on a napkin. Get the person's name. If they've made a deal with you, this will serve to prove it later. Even though the deal is illegal, the person may realize the best thing to do is comply rather than risk job loss/prosecution for "buying" organs from a hysterical relative who was clearly under duress.

Depending on who has died, your sense of humor and the kind of relationship you had with the dead person, you might want to see if you can do better. Keep in mind that it is illegal to pay people for their organs. But go ahead and try. Maybe you can visualize little Carol up in heaven laughing as her mom or dad jacks the body snatchers around? In this case, you've got to get the money or whatever you want right then and there and then leave the hospital. Do not accept checks. Your bargaining position disappears the minute you sign the consent forms (or the minute you alienate the procurers so much with your callous avarice that they say "fuck it" to little Carol's corneas).

Look around for something. Maybe that kindly nurse with her non-threatening body language is sporting a pair of diamond earrings. Maybe Father O'Flagherty is wearing a Rolex. How much cash can they scare up in the next hour or so? In the next twenty minutes?

This is a harsh, harsh method of making money and you really should only do it if you have prepared yourself ahead of time. Just know that you can do it. Organs are literally worth millions of dollars, but only for a short period of time.

Selling Fetal Tissue

Although a fetus is not an organ, I include it here because its latest uses are so similar to organ transplants and because fetal tissue implants are likely to become a very hot topic in the near future. And, after all, fetuses grow within a human body and then are removed. Many of the same features of organ transplants are also true of fetal tissue implants (type of cells that are useful, the necessity of finding correct donors, the importance of fresh tissues, etc.).

Many people find the entire subject repulsive. Abortion for some people is already repulsive and the idea that a fetus would be deliberately used for medical purposes instead of being allowed to grow into a child is abhorrent. The idea that money might change hands in the process just makes it that much more horrible.

On the other hand, not everybody thinks this way. Some people are thrilled by the prospect of using aborted fetuses to cure an unbelievably wide variety of extremely debilitating diseases such as Parkinson's disease, leukemia, diabetes, serious head injuries, broken spinal cords, strokes... the list is nearly endless. There may come a time when using fetal cells will be as important to western medicine as surgery or drugs.

I don't intend to address the ethical aspects of selling fetal tissue in this book. People must figure out for themselves where they stand. But here are the facts and some of the theories associated with fetal cell implantation.

The use of fetal cells resembles many other kinds of transplants and is not particularly complicated. Surgeons remove cells from the various organs of an aborted fetus six or seven weeks old (less than one inch long) and put them into the corresponding organ of the sick person. There, these highly adaptable cells thrive and repair or replace the damaged cells of the patient.

Fetal cells are less susceptible to rejection — they don't seem to care that they're in a "foreign" body, and adopt it as though it were their own. Cells taken from a fetal pancreas have been implanted into diabetics where they began pumping out insulin. Brain cells implanted into the heads of Parkinson's sufferers have relieved many of the problems associated with that disease.

Most experiments in the United States have been on animals, but human testing cannot be far off. The procedure promises to replace what are now risky and fairly unsuccessful operations such as pancreas transplants. A pancreas from a cadaver is a poor source of the insulin-producing cells called "The Islets of Langerhans." An adult pancreas is tough and gritty and the cells must be physically scraped away by hand — a process that invariably damages some of the cells. Fetal islets, by comparison, are easily removed from a very soft fetal pancreas.

The number of people who stand to benefit is staggering: more than half a million people are stricken with Parkinson's disease, a million people are severely afflicted with diabetes — a disease that normally leads to blindness, limb amputation and early death. Add to this the potential to save millions from senility, paralysis and some cancers, and you've got a powerful incentive to continue the research.

Fetal cells are prized primarily for their adaptability to other bodies. Rejection, which is a common problem in other organ transplants, simply is not that great a factor. Thus, using blood-producing fetal liver cells injected into the bloodstreams of people with blood disorders like leukemia doesn't provoke the strong and fatal rejection that so often occurs. This is good news to leukemia patients, three fourths of whom don't happen to have a sibling with the appropriate tissue type — so far the only viable source of liver cells.

This is not to say that fetal cells are totally interchangeable, but they don't require such a close match. Very close matches can, however, be made to order by female members of a patient's family or strangers with the same basic tissue types. As research continues in this field, the role of the fetus-provider will become more defined. It may be that "fetus banks" will be set up along the lines of sperm banks, matching, as exactly as possible, patients to fetus donors. For the time being, there does not appear to be a market for fetuses, since the field is still in its infancy and there is such a huge supply of aborted fetuses available for experimental use now.

4

Liquid Assets

Your body can also be a literal fountain of money. While selling blood (and these days, plasma) has been a traditional way for shirkers and outsiders to make money without working, there are other things your body produces that can be profitable too. Not only blood but hair, semen, eggs, and even human milk are all in demand by people with cash money.

Blood

We'll begin with blood since this is often a person's first time in the field of selling himself and since it is so well established. Try as they might, scientists just haven't been able to make synthetic blood. Blood is invaluable for making many pharmaceutical products that save and improve millions of lives. Vaccines, gammaglobulin, and clotting agents for hemophiliacs are only a few of the things that can be manufactured from human blood.

These days, however, it is virtually impossible to sell your blood. This practice was stopped many years ago when the Red Cross found that the quality of donated blood was far better (and cheaper) than blood they bought from winos. Besides, they never paid very much and you could only do it every six weeks, so it was never a very decent meal ticket for the donor.

Luckily, a nationwide for-profit system of blood plasma centers has sprung up and offers many advantages over selling blood. For one thing, you can do it as often as three times a week, earning $100 or more per month depending on the economics of the area and your dedication to be bled for plasma on a regular basis.

Because plasma "donation" (really it's vending, not donating) has become so commonplace, I won't bother going too deeply into the subject. The process is simple. After a short medical examination you sign up to become a regular donor. At regularly scheduled intervals you then come to the donation center and have a pint of your plasma removed through a vein in your arm.

Sometimes the examination is little more than an interview with some foreign doctor who for some reason has decided not to practice medicine but to talk to poor people about whether they've ever had hepatitis. These doctors are probably the same ones who get jobs watching people take urine tests. Obviously you're dealing with a strange character.

The test is often written, posed in yes/no format. Use your brain and answer what they want to hear. No, you've never had a homosexual experience; no, you haven't had your ear pierced within the last six months; and no, you don't take any medication at all. Then the doctor might glance at your body to see if you have any serious blotches or plague bubae and send you back out to the crowd. Next!

After the personnel seat you in a fairly comfortable couch-like piece of furniture and suck out a quantity of your blood, technicians then take the blood to a centrifuge which, by spinning, separates the red blood cells from the plasma. The red cells are then mixed with a saline solution and returned to your bloodstream via an intravenous tube. Then the process is repeated. In the end, you lose a pint of blood plasma, which the body can replace within three days. Then you come back.

This draining and refilling process used to take as much as three hours but newer machines can get the job done in 45 minutes. One of the most important things to remember is that you cannot move while this is going on. So make sure you go to the bathroom first and are otherwise prepared to stay put. It is also a good idea to bring something to read or perhaps a personal stereo with headphones.

Plasma companies pay on a sliding scale designed to encourage you to come back and become a regular source of plasma. They normally increase the payments for plasma in cycles and penalize you if you only come in sporadically.

It should be stressed that this operation is not without some real risk, even though the folks at the donation center will assure you you're safe. They will try to make it sound as if your plasma is a sort of liquid version of your appendix that you don't really need. They'll point out how quickly the body replaces lost plasma — implying that this is because it's so easy for the body to make. This is not true.

In all fairness, they do take extraordinary precautions not to mix up blood and end up killing someone. They test your blood each and every time you come in, to find out whether or not you've got any diseases, too. This is for their benefit, not yours — certain diseases such as hepatitis make your plasma unsalable and worthless to them.

So, where is the real danger in plasma donation? You should know that your body does not manufacture plasma for no good reason. Plasma is the medium in which your red blood cells move. It is the fluid part of blood, which would otherwise be a dry heap of red cells looking like so much red dust. One of the reasons it's replaced so fast is it is so necessary to your survival.

Plasma also contains valuable antibodies you definitely need to fight off diseases ranging from a cold to meningitis. When you lose your plasma at a donation center you certainly come out weaker than you went in and more susceptible to getting sick. You also have fairly dramatically altered the blood's protein level and should seek to replace it soon. Eating a big steak is one way to help yourself out, even though it sort of defeats the purpose of selling plasma, since steak is so expensive. Eating a few eggs is just as good.

To prove what I have just said about how valuable your plasma is in warding off illness, consider this: plasma companies will often pay five or ten times the normal amount for plasma from someone who has mononucleosis. Plasma from a person with this disease is loaded with antibodies and hence, worth more. Use this information as you will. If you want to increase the value of your plasma, do what you can to come down with mononucleosis — but be aware that it will take you longer to get well if you hand over your plasma during your illness.

Plasma donation centers can be found in the yellow pages of your phone book. In many cities, there is some stiff competition between the businesses, so shop around for the one that gets you the best deal.

There is perhaps another use for blood that could bring a pretty penny...

Just as people can sell "clean" urine guaranteed to pass drug tests, you might be able to make similar use of your blood. For example, there could easily be a market for

AIDS-free blood, since the presence of HIV virus can wreak havoc with a person's life even beyond the illness. Insurance companies won't insure you, employers won't hire you... it's a mess. To help out, you could offer to stand in for the person at his test. Nobody checks IDs at clinics to make sure it's the right person.

On the other hand, having AIDS also has some benefits. You can sometimes get disability checks, you can often use the virus to scare people into giving you what you want or to win sympathy for strategic purposes. If you get thrown in jail you can often get special accommodations because you have AIDS. The same theory can be applied to other diseases you may wish you could test positive for, so don't overlook any opportunities to sell even "bad" blood.

Sperm

Getting paid for jacking off is every teenage boy's dream. These days it's easier than ever to realize this elusive goal. Dozens of sperm banks are listed in Appendix Six. For more information on egg and sperm donation contact:

Fertility Research Foundation
1430 Second Avenue, Suite 103
New York, NY 10021   (212) 744-5500

You don't have to be an Einstein with blond hair and blue eyes to milk your body of its money making potential. Sperm banks need a complete inventory of genetic material on hand, from a five foot, hirsute wrestler to a slender, red-headed basketball player. This is because fathers don't like it to be too obvious that they aren't the biological fathers of their children. So sperm banks need all types.

Intelligence is not measured at every sperm bank. As testing for IQ becomes less and less trusted as a measure of intelligence, other methods of determining intelligence are being used. One lab listed here neither measures IQ nor does it cater to women looking for a specific intelligence rating.

Still, it's a good idea to avoid looking like a moron when bucking to become father of potentially hundreds of kids.

Most sperm banks make their money selling donated sperm to women who want to have children but, for one reason or another, can't or won't get a man to do it with. Often it is because the husband's sperm count is too low to ensure an offspring or perhaps he carries a genetic disease that he doesn't feel like bequeathing to his kids. For whatever reason, thousands of women undergo various types of artificial insemination all over the country. To that end, there have sprung up sperm banks. Super-frozen in their vaults are the gooey building blocks of future generations, ready for thawing and implantation into a willing uterus.

Customers simply thumb through a catalog of donors (no names are used) until they find the type of father they want, then ante up the hundreds of dollars per session it takes to get pregnant.

A few years ago, most artificial inseminations made use of the jism of medical students tapping their resources in a room adjacent to another room in which the intended host lay on a steel table with her legs splayed. Fresh sperm donation is a thing of the past. In some states it is even illegal. The fear of AIDS and other diseases has made this route too scary for most.

For you, the "donor," all this is academic. All you really need to worry about is getting accepted at a bank and making sure your sperm count is high. Being good-looking and having college degrees is a plus, but certainly not necessary. One owner of a sperm bank told me he likes to recruit college students since, he figures, if they're smart enough to make their way through higher education they should be pretty solid, brain-wise. Since more than 60% of white males of college age have at least some college, it's easy to see this guy is not too picky.

Still, when applying for this job, make sure you look clean and bright. In this case your first impression may be your only impression. When speaking with an interviewer, speak clearly and don't try talking any jive. It's enough to seem alert and conversational. Don't look at the ceiling or spend the whole time with your mouth open, engrossed in twisting a paper clip into festive shapes.

Once you get accepted they'll want you to jack off for them, possibly right then, or they may tell you not to spoo for a couple of days and come back. Sperm banks are looking for potent sperm, so they need at least three days build-up. You'd be surprised at how unreliable sperms can be. As many as one out of five sperms will be defective. If you're lucky the bank will let you have a gander at your semen. You'll be amazed to see obviously deformed cells: sperms with two heads, sperms with tails sticking out of their sides, or sperms that appear paralyzed and may be dead. At least 30 million motile, healthy sperms are needed for a single insemination. The build-up helps ensure this count.

You'll probably have to do your jacking off on the premises in some private closet-type place they've set up for this purpose. I have (no shit) heard these little cubby holes referred to as "masturbatoriums." Whatever they call it, it will probably contain a supply of pornography, a sink, and some kind of lubricant, if you like that sort of thing.

You beat off into a test tube, then zip up your fly and hand it to the nice man outside. He is also the one who will issue you a check or maybe even pay you in cash. All records are kept strictly confidential and some places even refer to you by your number at all times. The going rate for a shot of good sperm is about $50.

Your income will depend on how much your semen is in demand. As you can see by the sample sheet from one sperm bank's catalog (see Appendix Five), there are a lot of samples on hand from some guys and not so many from others. This not only reflects how much money sperm donors are making, it also shows something of the variety of types needed. Note the wide range of occupations and interests listed. If you are a reasonably successful sperm donor, you may be able to donate a couple of times a month.

Make sure when you donate you have something to donate. This basically means having a high sperm count, which can normally only be achieved by at least three days abstinence. Each and every sperm sample is examined under a microscope before they dish out the money for it. A low count might mean you just went through all this for nothing. So don't think you can get away with fucking in the morning and donating semen that afternoon. It's practically impossible. You can try pushing it a little bit to see where your minimum time is, since not every guy is the same. Just do it slowly or you'll get labelled unreliable and not asked back.

Another tip to enhance your sperm count is to keep your balls at a relatively cool temperature. Testicles function best at a couple of degrees below normal body temperature, which is why they're hanging outside your body in a scrotum in the first place. But, too much cold can also adversely affect sperm production (notice how your balls scrunch up when the temperature dips?), so avoid that too. While trying to build up your sperm, stay away from tight pants, and saunas, or any other situation of extreme temperature.

Cryogenic Experiments

Ugly, retarded guys can make money off their sperm, too. Maybe even more, since far more sperm is used in freezing experiments that require only a certain amount of live sperm. They don't even care if you have AIDS!

This is perhaps the most lucrative market for selling your sperm. Best of all, it is also the most unknown. All over the country, research centers are doing experiments with cryogenics (freezing and storing) to develop ways to keep sperm in suspended animation for long periods without damaging the cells. Currently, most sperm is kept cool by immersion in liquid nitrogen, but a goodly number of the sperm cells don't survive the freezing and thawing, and thus, the bank ends up with "damaged goods."

Some of the places that buy sperm for experimentation are listed in Appendix Six, but the list is not exhaustive. A few calls around to hospitals in big cities can get you current information on who is in the market for your baby batter.

Since these places don't plan to impregnate anyone with the sperm, it's far less important that you be smart. You'll only have to know how to beat off. They will also allow you to make your "donation" at home, as long as you get it to them within an hour of jizzing. And, at $25 a shot, this can be a real money-maker, since they'll allow you to donate as often as every 48 hours. These opportunities are rarely advertised, so you have to go looking for them, but it's well worth the effort. Happy hunting.

Milk

Lilja Virtanen, a 28-year-old mother from the town of Jyvreskylae, Finland, won that country's medal of merit after producing her 300th liter of wholesome milk for use in a local hospital. She was credited with saving the lives of more than 20 premature babies. In addition to breast-feeding her son, the prodigious woman had enough left over that she could sell it to the hospital.

Sell it? Yep. She continued to nurse her son and sold any leftover milk for about $5 per liter, tax-free. This means

Lilja not only got the medal but at least some $1,500 for her milk.

Unfortunately, in this country, you won't get a medal unless you kill someone, and the only people allowed to sell milk are the fake-milk companies. Still, there is a market for human milk in this country.

Many hospitals run milk banks where they store excess human milk to feed to newborns whose mothers for some reason cannot breast-feed them. This milk can be especially important in helping premature babies survive. But these babies are quickly weaned onto artificial formula and sent home. Of course the hospitals charge money for the milk, but they don't pay the woman who gave it anything at all.

Now everybody knows that human milk is preferable to formula and the best milk of all comes from your own mother. A woman's milk is especially well formulated for her own baby and the composition of her milk will even change to meet the nutritional needs of the child as he grows.

Despite this, it's still considered sort of bizarre for a woman to breast-feed (not as bad as thirty years ago when the formula companies had convinced us that human milk was inferior to their product), or if not bizarre, then at least counter-culture, hence groups like La Leche League. La Leche League was formed (and has groups all over the country now) to promote breast-feeding, and holds regular meetings for mothers who want to make sure their child gets the best.

I contacted one of the high mucky-mucks in La Leche and posed the question to her about how one might go about selling human milk. She was not at all averse to the idea — after all, the tradition of the "wet-nurse" is an old one. Black slaves often breast-fed the white offspring of their mistresses when it was considered unseemly or perhaps merely inconvenient for the lady to do so. At times people have been hired to feed someone else's child in exchange for... money.

Selling your milk to a milk bank is unfeasible. Milk banks don't pay anything, have stringent rules about how the milk can be donated, and to top it off, milk doesn't keep very well. Undoubtedly this could change in a free market but for the moment, the best way to make money off your breast-milk is to become a wet-nurse.

The first place to go is your local La Leche League and ask them for help. Let them know you've got milk to spare and would like to sell it. To avoid any problems with laws controlling the sale of milk and everything else, make sure you charge only for — "babysitting." Or perhaps you could arrange a milk-trade with another nursing mother with whom you can share milk, thus giving each other a break while making sure the kid never has to suck on a bottle.

Another idea is to take out an ad in a newspaper. I recommend one of the so-called "alternative" news weeklies available in nearly every city. They are avidly read by well-to-do youngish folks who often contract out almost all the chores in their lives. If they'll pay to have someone come in and organize their closet, why wouldn't they pay for someone to breast-feed their child?

5

Chunky Bits

Eggs

Up until very recently, there was no market for women's eggs comparable to that for men's sperm — that is now changing. The market is lucrative. Fertility centers charge an average of $10,000 for each attempt at a pregnancy with donated eggs. Normally, it takes more than one attempt to achieve pregnancy. In fact, four or five tries is about average. It was only a matter of time before the donors started to wonder why they were the only ones not getting paid.

Customers for donated eggs are often women who have reached menopause, have difficulty getting pregnant, or perhaps don't want to risk a genetic deformity passed on by heredity or by age. There is the "stale egg" theory that helps to explain why birth defects are more common in children born to women over age 40.

Enter the robust young gal with her young ovaries overflowing with tens of thousands of healthy, juicy eggs.

The process is much like sperm donation, including the guarantee of anonymity. (It should be noted here that this anonymity is a two way street. You're not going to be able to find out where "your" children are. Ever. Once you've sold your sperm or eggs, you are out of the picture. Nobody is supposed to track you down, and you're going to return the favor.) It's only at the donation stage of the game that the procedure differs.

And it differs a lot. For one thing, instead of a measly $50, women get around $2,000 for their eggs. But then again, the procedure is more time-consuming, risky and painful.

First, egg vendors must undergo a series of hormone injections to stimulate their ovaries to release more eggs. They must also undergo ultrasound scans to determine when the time is ripe to harvest their eggs. While neither of these procedures is particularly painful, they are somewhat of a nuisance. At least a sperm donor gets to have an orgasm when he visits the clinic!

Then comes the harvesting. For this the woman must be put under general anesthesia and the eggs are harvested via a tiny incision in the lower abdomen. Recovery is quick, with minimal pain.

At the moment, there are some 48 medical centers in the country that will perform this operation (including the insertion of the eggs into another woman's uterus). Most insist that women bring their own donors. Only a few places on the East and West coasts bother to provide donors. The most prominent of these centers is the one at the University of Southern California.

The fact that so few places make donors available to women who want to buy eggs makes it easier, not harder, to find a buyer. Since so many hospitals are willing and able to perform all the necessary operations, it's only necessary to take an ad out in a local paper, advertising your eggs. Since the practice is relatively new, perhaps you could pull some kind of publicity stunt to get attention. In any case, there is a demand for eggs that is going unfilled and the market is there.

And you may donate more than once. Since females are born with about 40,000 eggs, it is difficult to imagine her running short just because she sells a few — even if a few hundred are extracted in each operation.

Hair

Humans all over the world grow an abundant crop of hair. Normally this hair gets cut off, falls to the floor, and is swept into the trash. Some people mix it with clay to make bricks. It is, of course, possible to weave it into yarn. It could probably even be used to make gelatin — but it isn't. Most hair just gets thrown away. Unless it is used for wigs or for practice models in beauty schools.

Beauty schools almost exclusively get their hair from the Far East. Oriental hair is very thick compared to Caucasian hair. It is also very straight, which means it's ideal for learning how to make curls, do permanents, etc. Being so thick, it is tougher, too, and can withstand repeated washings and chemical treatments, etc. There is no real market for American hair for sale to beauty schools.

But there is a large market for Caucasian hair for use in human hair wigs and toupees. Unfortunately, that market is almost exclusively European, specifically Eastern European, where hair collectors make regular and gigantic rounds harvesting hair from entire villages every two years.

In some places, growing hair is something of a family business.

Northern Italy, too, is a prime place to get good human hair. America is a horrible place to get it.

That's because in Europe, they don't wash their hair as often, nor treat it with harsh chemicals and dyes that strip away a lot of the hair's outer layers and render it weaker and weaker. Europeans also tend to spend less time in the harsh sunlight. Out in the rural villages, most women keep their hair covered much of the time, further preserving it for use in wigs. American wig-makers get most of their hair from Europe.

However, there is one place in the United States that will buy your hair. Hair Addictions Inc. in Seattle, Washington, seems to be the lone hair-buyer for the whole country. Hair Addictions' Paul Greenpalm says he'll buy anyone's hair as long as it's a minimum of 18 inches long and in decent shape. Depending on the quality, he pays between $10 and $20 an ounce. A head full of long hair can weigh 4-8 ounces, so it's not unreasonable that an ex-hippie might make a hundred bucks or so by getting a crew cut.

It's important to meet Paul's requirements before you cut off your hair and send it to him. He's thrown away perfectly good hair merely because it has been improperly cut and packaged. Ideally you should go to his shop, but he doesn't mind if you put it in a box and mail it to him.

Besides being at least 18 inches long (the longer the better), the hair must all face the same direction, so don't just hack it off and throw it in a box willy-nilly. Bind the hank of freshly cut hair with rubber bands (at either end) and send it off. If he likes it, he'll buy it. Contact Paul Greenpalm at:

Hair Addictions
13240 North East 20th
Bellevue, WA 98005   (206) 644-4460

A note of caution. Most Americans abuse their hair with detergents, bleach, and dyes. This could easily render your hair useless for a wig. So will split ends, an indication of damaged hair. If you have oily hair, so much the better.

Urine, Dandruff, Mucus, Sweat, Tears, Etc.

Of course, your body produces plenty of other products. Unfortunately, there is little market for any of them. Although "clean" urine is sold by a couple of different companies, they appear to have an ample supply and are not on the lookout for any more. You could, of course, market your urine to someone interested in a golden shower, but this falls within the realm of plain old prostitution and thus is beyond the scope of this book.

But don't get depressed. There are new markets springing up all the time. There could be a colony of very valuable microbes living under your fingernails that for all you know will produce a cure for cancer — or even be used as a new artificial sweetener!

6

Two Forms of Legal Prostitution

Harvesting the Child Within

Having a uterus is like a license to print money. Conceiving, carrying, and giving birth to other people's babies is a lucrative business. The minimum amount a surrogate mother should get for her trouble is a clear $10,000, with all related medical expenses paid. It's not unreasonable for some women to get more than $30,000 for the use of their wombs. And there are thousands of people willing to pay a woman to have a child for them.

There are at least ten ways to get pregnant without having sex, all of them designed to overcome the problem of infertility. Eggs and sperm can be mixed in vitro (in a test tube) then placed into anyone's womb where it will hopefully latch onto the wall and begin growing. Childless couples who cannot have children will go to any length to have a kid, and adoption is not their first choice. A lot of the people who are willing to adopt a baby are white and would like a healthy white baby. This is not, however, what is most available, so the wait for a healthy, white baby to adopt can be years.

While baby-selling per se is illegal, it is generally not illegal to agree to carry another person's child for them. This practice has been around for years, and it's sparked a lot of controversy and a lot of legislation in that time. Which is why it's not possible to adequately cover this topic in this book.

Almost every day there is another new wrinkle in the laws that govern this practice, mainly arising out of arguments between people who've changed their minds. Surrogate mothers often decide that they don't want to give up the kid. Sometimes there's something wrong with the kid and the customers decide not to take delivery of their child. It is a royal mess since, although the contracts are invalid (even illegal) in some states, the courts must still decide who must care for the child.

Generally, surrogate mothers cannot win custody of the children they conceive, although a recent ruling in California did award part-time custody to a surrogate who carried a child for a couple who divorced after she was hired. But previous rulings in California have awarded children to whomever gave birth to the child (this is the normal definition of a mother according to state law), except for at least once when a surrogate mother lost custody of the child she bore, since both the egg and the sperm were donated by the people who hired her.

And this is only in California.

The same kind of battles are taking place in every state. As it stands now there is virtually no solid body of law or even common customs to regulate surrogate motherhood.

So, the advice here is: go to the library and get the most recent books possible on the subject, consult a lawyer, and be aware that this can be a tricky process. The best way to make the deal go smoothly is to abide by the contract. This is often easier said than done, because of the enormous psychological implications of having children. In addition, you should know that the paying parents have a right to require you to abstain from alcohol, smoking, or whatever else they think will be bad for their baby. Although some women's groups are objecting to the view that a surrogate mother is no more than an incubator, there is no other way to look at it at present. Make sure you understand fully the terms of any agreement. Once you've decided... sleep on it.

Selling Your Time/Labor

This is, of course, one of the most common ways to rent yourself for cash. Recent studies indicate millions of people earn their living by having jobs — so it might seem like a good idea for you, too.

But having a job can be very demanding, if not dangerous. Some 70,000 people die on the job each year in work-related "accidents." One type of accident that afflicts people who get jobs in the "service sector" is murder. Sure, getting a job at a convenience store or a gas station might pay as much as four bucks an hour (plus all the Slim Jims you can eat) but you should factor in the hidden costs. Service sector jobs often require you to wear a buffoonish uniform and endure obnoxious members of the general public before they shoot or disfigure you.

If you get an industrial-type job you risk exposure to assembly lines, time clocks, and bitter vending machine coffee. Many such job holders are required to breathe poisonous chemicals and perform repetitive tasks that damage their nerves, muscles and ligaments, causing extreme pain as boredom slowly drives them insane. Lots of workers are permanently disabled on the job from falls, burns, or having a limb caught in some heavy machinery. Some job holders contract fatal illnesses from their job environments, suffocate in tunnel cave-ins, or are electrocuted to death.

Even in white-collar jobs there are hidden dangers, like daily freeway traffic, office politics and the hell of looking busy to please a boss. And you still will be confronted with repetitive stress injuries and bitter vending machine coffee. You will also often be required to wear a tie and "be on time." They divide the work day into no fewer than 480 minutes and you must account for each and every one of them.

In addition, many companies arrange their jobs in such a way that a person's work product can be measured by the amount of abuse heaped on his subordinates. This can be pretty rough if you have to start out at the bottom. It can be rough even if you start out near the top.

It seems slightly better in the military. Soldiers are paid more than the minimum wage, but you still have to wear a buffoonish uniform. It's true that military jobs are "safer" (fewer people shoot at you) and you cannot be fired very easily, but if your boss gets angry he can send you to prison for twenty years with the stroke of a pen. Often this punishment is doled out for what is known as "having a bad attitude." There is also the very real chance that you will be called upon to kill your fellow man because of his "bad attitude" — office politics carried to its extreme.

All in all, it's just not worth it to earn money by taking a job — with one exception.

Although some argue it is more of a scam, the only job I can recommend in good conscience is that of a college professor. The hours are short, pay is high and you have grading power over a great number of sexually active young people.

Appendix One

Federal Law Regarding
Protection of Human Test Subjects

Part 50 — Protection of
Human Subjects

Subpart A - General Provisions

Sec.
50.1 Scope.
50.3 Definitions.

Subpart B-Informed Consent
of Human Subjects

50.20 General requirements for informed consent.
50.21 Effective date.
50.23 Exception from general requirements.
50.25 Elements of informed consent.
50.27 Documentation of informed consent.

Subpart C-Protections Pertaining to
Clinical Investigations Involving
Prisoners as Subjects

50.40 Applicability.
50.42 Purpose.

50.44 Restrictions on clinical investigations involving prisoners.
50.46 Composition of institutional review boards where prisoners are involved.
50.48 Additional duties of the institutional review boards where prisoners are involved.

AUTHORITY: Secs. 406, 409, 502, 503, 505, 506, 507, 510, 513-516, 518-520, 701(a), 706 and 801, Pub. L. 717 52 Stat. 1049-1054 as amended. 1055, 1058 as amended, 55 Stat. 851 as amended. 59 Stat. 463 as amended. 72 Stat. 1785-1788 as amended, 74 Stat. 399-407 as amended, 76 Stat. 794-795 as amended, 90 Stat. 540-560, 562-574 (21 U.S.C. 346, 348, 352, 353, 355, 356, 357, 360, 360c-360f, 360h-360j, 371(a), 376, and 381); secs. 215, 351, 354-360F, Pub. L. 410, 58 Stat. 690, 702 as amended, 82 Stat. 1173-1186 as amended (42 U.S.C. 216, 262, 263b-263n), unless otherwise noted.

SOURCE: 45 FR 36390, May 30, 1980, unless otherwise noted.

Subpart A — General Provisions

§ 50.1 Scope.

(a) This part applies to all clinical investigations regulated by the Food and Drug Administration under sections 505(i), 507(d), and 520(g) of the Federal Food, Drug, and Cosmetic Act, as well as clinical investigations that support applications for research or marketing permits for products regulated by the Food and Drug Administration, including food and color additives, drugs for human use, medical devices for human use, biological products for human use, and electronic products. Additional specific obligations and commitments of, and standards of conduct for, persons who sponsor or monitor clinical investigations involving particular test articles may also be found in other parts (e.g., Parts 312 and 812). Compliance with these parts is intended to protect the rights and safety of subjects involved in investigations filed with the Food and Drug Administration pursuant to sections 406, 409, 502, 503, 505, 506, 507, 510, 513-516, 518-520, 706, and 801 of the Federal Food, Drug, and Cosmetic Act and sections 351 and 354-360F of the Public Health Service Act.

(b) References in this part to regulatory sections of the Code of Federal Regulations are to Chapter I of Title 21, unless otherwise noted.

[45 FR 36390, May 30, 1980; 46 FR 8979, Jan. 27, 1981]

§ 50.3 Definitions.

As used in this part:

(a) "Act" means the Federal Food, Drug, and Cosmetic Act, as amended (secs. 201-902, 52 Stat. 1040 et seq. as amended (21 U.S.C. 321-392)).

(b) "Application for research or marketing permit" includes:

(1) A color additive petition, described in Part 71.

(2) A food additive petition, described in Parts 171 and 571.

(3) Data and information about a substance submitted as part of the procedures for establishing that the substance is generally recognized as safe for use that results or may reasonably be expected to result, directly or indirectly, in its becoming a component or otherwise affecting the characteristics of any food, described in §§ 170.30 and 570.30.

(4) Data and information about a food additive submitted as part of the procedures for food additives permitted to be used on an interim basis pending additional study, described in § 180.1.

(5) Data and information about a substance submitted as part of the procedures for establishing a tolerance for unavoidable contaminants in food and food-packaging materials, described in section 406 of the act.

(6) A "Notice of Claimed Investigational Exemption for a New Drug," described in Part 312.

(7) A new drug application, described in Part 314.

(8) Data and information about the bioavailability or bioequivalence of drugs for human use submitted as part of the procedures for issuing, amending or repealing a bioequivalence requirement, described in Part 320.

(9) Data and information about an over-the-counter drug for human use submitted as part of the procedures for classifying these drugs as generally recognized as safe and effective and not misbranded, described in Part 330.

(10) Data and information about a prescription drug for human use submitted as part of the procedures for classifying these drugs and generally recognized as safe and effective and not misbranded, described in this chapter.

(11) Data and information about an antibiotic drug submitted as part of the procedures for issuing, amending, or repealing

regulations for these drugs, described in Part 430.

(12) An application for a biological product license, described in Part 601.

(13) Data and information about a biological product submitted as part of the procedures for determining that licensed biological products are safe and effective and not misbranded, described in Part 601.

(14) Data and information about an in vitro diagnostic product submitted as part of the procedures for establishing, amending, ord repealing a standard for these products, described in Part 809.

(15) An "Application for an Investigational Device Exemption," described in Part 812.

(16) Data and information about a medical device submitted as part of the procedures for classifying these devices, described in section 513.

(17) Data and information about a medical device submitted as part of the procedures for establishing, amending, or repealing a standard for these devices, described in section 514.

(18) An application for premarket approval of a medical device, described in section 515.

(19) A product development protocol for a medical device, described in section 515.

(20) Data and information about an electronic product submitted as part of the procedures for establishing, amending, or repealing a standard for these products, described in section 358 of the Public Health Service Act.

(21) Data and information about an electronic product submitted as part of the procedures for obtaining a variance from any electronic product performance standard, as described in § 1010.4.

(22) Data and information about an electronic product submitted as part of the procedures for granting, amending, or extending an exemption from a radiation safe-

ty performance standard, as described in § 1010.5.

(c) "Clinical investigation" means any experiment that involves a test article and one or more human subjects and that either is subject to requirements for prior submission to the Food and Drug Administration under section 505(i), 507(d), or 520(g) of the act, or is not subject to requirements for prior submission to the Food and Drug Administration under these sections of the act, but the results of which are intended to be submitted later to, or held for inspection by, the Food and Drug Administration as part of an application for a research or marketing permit. The term does not include experiments that are subject to the provisions of Part 58 of this chapter, regarding nonclinical laboratory studies.

(d) "Investigator" means an individual who actually conducts a clinical investigation, i.e., under whose immediate direction the test article is administered or dispensed to, or used involving, a subject, or, in the event of an investigation conducted by a team of individuals, is the responsible leader of that team.

(e) "Sponsor" means a person who initiates a clinical investigation, but who does not actually conduct the investigation, i.e., the test article is administered or dispensed to or used involving, a subject under the immediate direction of another individual. A person other than an individual (e.g., corporation or agency) that uses one or more of its own employees to conduct a clinical investigation it has initiated is considered to be a sponsor (not a sponsor-investigator), and the employees are considered to be investigators.

(f) "Sponsor-investigator" means an individual who both initiates and actually conducts, alone or with others, a clinical investigation, i.e., under whose immediate direction the test article is administered or dispensed to, or used involving, a subject. The term does not include any person other than an individual, e.g., corporation or agency.

(g) "Human subject" means an individual who is or becomes a participant in research, either as a recipient of the test article or as a control. A subject may be either a healthy human or a patient.

(h) "Institution" means any public or private entity or agency (including Federal, State, and other agencies). The word "facility" as used in section 520(g) of the act is deemed to be synonymous with the term "institution" for purposes of this part.

(i) "Institutional review board" (IRB) means any board, committee, or other group formally designated by an institution to review biomedical research involving humans as subjects, to approve the initiation of and conduct periodic review of such research. The term has the same meaning as the phrase "institutional review committee" as used in section 520(g) of the act.

(j) "Prisoner" means any individual involuntarily confined or detained in a penal institution. The term is intended to encompass individuals sentenced to such an institution under a criminal or civil statute, individuals detained in other facilities by virtue of statutes or commitment procedures that provide alternatives to criminal prosecution or incarceration in a penal institution, and individuals detained pending arraignment, trial, or sentencing.

(k) "Test article" means any drug (including a biological product for human use), medical device for human use, human food additive, color additive, electronic product, or any other article subject to regulation under the act or under sections 351 or 354-360F of the Public Health Service Act (42 U.S.C. 262 and 263b-263n).

(l) "Minimal risk" means that the risks of harm anticipated in the proposed research are not greater, considering probability and magnitude, than those ordinarily encountered in daily life or during the performance of routine physical or psychological examinations or tests.

(m) "Legally authorized representative" means an individual or judicial or other body authorized under applicable law to consent on behalf of a prospective subject to the subject's participation in the procedure(s) involved in the research.

(Secs. 406, 408, 409, 502, 503, 505, 506, 507, 510, 513-516, 518-520, 701(a), 706, and 801. 52 Stat. 1049-1053 as amended, 1055, 1058 as amended, 55 Stat. 851 as amended, 59 Stat. 463 as amended, 68 Stat. 511-517 as amended, 72 Stat. 1785-1788 as amended. 74 Stat. 399-407 as amended, 76 Stat. 794-795 as amended, 90 Stat. 540-560, 562-574 (21 U.S.C. 346, 346a, 348, 352, 353, 355, 356, 357, 360, 360c-360f, 360h-360j, 371(a), 376, and 381); secs. 215, 301, 351, 354-360F, 58 Stat. 690, 702 as amended, 82 Stat. 1173-1186 as amended (42 U.S.C. 216, 241, 262, 263b-263n))

[45 FR 36390, May 30, 1980, as amended at 46 FR 8950, Jan. 27, 1981]

Subpart B - Informed Consent of Human Subjects

AUTHORITY: Secs. 406, 408, 409, 502, 503, 505, 506, 507, 510, 513,-516, 518-520, 701(a), 706, and 801, 52 Stat. 1049-1053 as amended, 1055, 1058 as amended, 55 Stat. 851 as amended, 59 Stat. 463 as amended, 68 Stat. 511-517 as amended, 72 Stat. 1785-1788 as amended, 74 Stat. 399-407 as amended, 76 Stat. 794-795 as amended, 90 Stat. 540-560, 562-574 (21 U.S.C. 346, 346a, 348, 352, 353, 355, 356, 357, 360,, 360c-360f, 360h-360j, 371(a), 376, and 381); secs. 215, 301, 351, 354-360F, 58 Stat. 690, 702 as amended, 82 Stat. 1173-1186 as amended (42 U.S.C. 216, 241, 262, 263b-263n)).

SOURCE: 46 FR 8951, Jan. 27, 1981 unless otherwise noted.

§50.20 General requirements for informed consent.

Except as provided in § 50.23, no investigator may involve a human being as a subject in research covered by these regulations unless the investigator has obtained the legally effective informed consent of the subject or the subject's legally authorized representative. An investigator shall seek such consent only under circumstances that provide the prospective subject or the representative sufficient opportunity to consider whether or not to participate and that minimize the possibility of coercion or undue influence. The information that is given to the subject or the representative shall be in language understandable to the subject or the representative. No informed consent, whether oral or written, may include any exculpatory language through which the subject or the representative is made to waive or appear to waive any of the subject's legal rights, or releases or appears to release the investigator, the sponsor, the institution, or its agents from liability for negligence.

§ 50.21 Effective date.

The requirements for informed consent set out in this part apply to all human subjects entering a clinical investigation that commences on or after July 27, 1981.

§ 50.23 Exception from general requirements.

(a) The obtaining of informed consent shall be deemed feasible unless, before use of the test article (except as provided in paragraph (b) of this section), both the investigator and a physician who is not otherwise participating in the clinical investigation certify in writing all of the following:

(1) The human subject is confronted by a life-threatening situation necessitating the use of the test article.

(2) Informed consent cannot be obtained from the subject because of an inability to communicate with, or obtain legally effective consent from, the subject.

(3) Time is not sufficient to obtain consent from the subject's legal representative.

(4) There is available no alternative method of approved or generally recognized

therapy that provides an equal or greater likelihood of saving the life of the subject.

(b) If immediate use of the test article is, in the investigator's opinion, required to preserve the life of the subject, and time is not sufficient to obtain the independent determination required in paragraph (a) of this section in advance of using the test article, the determinations of the clinical investigator shall be made and, within 5 working days after the use of the article, be reviewed and evaluated in writing by a physician who is not participating in the clinical investigation.

(c) The documentation required in paragraph (a) or (b) of this section shall be submitted to the IRB within 5 working days after the use of the test article.

§ 50.25 Elements of informed consent.

(a) *Basic elements of informed consent.* In seeking informed consent, the following information shall be provided to each subject:

(1) A statement that the study involves research, an explanation of the purposes of the research and the expected duration of the subject's participation, a description of the procedures to be followed, and identification of any procedures which are experimental.

(2) A description of any reasonably foreseeable risks or discomforts to the subject.

(3) A description of any benefits to the subject or to others which may reasonably be expected from the research.

(4) A disclosure of appropriate alternative procedures or courses of treatment, if any, that might be advantageous to the subject.

(5) A statement describing the extent, if any, to which confidentiality of records identifying the subject will be maintained and that notes the possibility that the Food and Drug Administration may inspect the records.

(6) For research involving more than minimal risk, an explanation as to whether any compensation and an explanation as to whether any medical treatments are available if injury occurs and, if so, what they consist of, or where further information may be obtained.

(7) An explanation of whom to contact for answers to pertinent questions about the research and research subjects' rights, and whom to contact in the event of a research-related injury to the subject.

(8) A statement that participation is voluntary, that refusal to participate will involve no penalty or loss of benefits to which the subject is otherwise entitled, and that the subject may discontinue participation at any time without penalty or loss of benefits to which the subject is otherwise entitled.

(b) *Additional elements of informed consent.* When appropriate, one or more of the following elements of information shall also be provided to each subject:

(1) A statement that the particular treatment or procedure may involve risks to the subject (or to the embryo or fetus, if the subject is or may become pregnant) which are currently unforeseeable.

(2) Anticipated circumstances under which the subject's participation may be terminated by the investigator without regard to the subject's consent.

(3) Any additional costs to the subject that may result from participation in the research.

(4) The consequences of a subject's decision to withdraw from the research and procedures for orderly termination of participation by the subject.

(5) A statement that significant new findings developed during the course of the research which may relate to the subject's willingness to continue participation will be provided to the subject.

(6) The approximate number of subjects involved in the study.

(c) The informed consent requirements in these regulations are not intended to preempt any applicable Federal, State, or local laws which require additional information to be disclosed for informed consent to be legally effective.

(d) Nothing in these regulations is intended to limit the authority of a physician to provide emergency medical care to the extent the physician is permitted to do so under applicable Federal, State and local law.

§ 50.27 Documentation of informed consent.

(a) Except as provided in § 56.109(c), informed consent shall be documented by the use of a written consent form approved by the IRB and signed by the subject or the subject's legally authorized representative. A copy shall be given to the person signing the form.

(b) Except as provided in § 56.109(c) the consent form may be either of the following:

(1) A written consent document that embodies the elements of informed consent required by § 50.25. This form may be read to the subject or the subject's legally authorized representative, but, in any event, the investigator shall give either the subject or the representative adequate opportunity to read it before it is signed.

(2) A "short form" written consent document stating that the elements of informed consent required by § 50.25 have been presented orally to the subject or the subject's legally authorized representative. When this method is used, there shall be a witness to the oral presentation. Also, the IRB shall approve a written summary of what is to be said to the subject or the representative. Only ihe short form itself is to be signed by the subject or the representative. However, the witness shall sign both the short form and a copy of the summary, and the person actually obtaining the consent shall sign a copy of the summary. A copy of the summary shall be given to the

subject or the representative in addition to a copy of the short form.

Subpart C-Protections Pertaining to Clinical Investigations Involving Prisoners as Subjects

EFFECTIVE DATE NOTE: At 46 FR 35085, July 7, 1981, the effective date of Subpart C was stayed until further notice.

§ 50.40 Applicability.

(a) The regulations in this subpart apply to all clinical investigations involving prisoners as subjects that are regulated by the Food and Drug Administration under sections 505(i), 507(d), or 520(g) of the Federal Food, Drug, and Cosmetic Act, as well as clinical investigations involving prisoners that support applications for research or marketing permits for products regulated by the Food and Drug Administration.

(b) Nothing in this subpart shall be construed as indicating that compliance with the procedures set forth herein will authorize research involving prisoners as subjects to the extent such research is limited or barred by applicable State or local law.

§ 50.42 Purpose.

Inasmuch as prisoners may be under constraints because of their incarceration which could affect their ability to make a truly voluntary and uncoerced decision whether or not to participate as subjects in research, it is the purpose of this subpart to provide additional safeguards for the protection of prisoners involved in activities to which this subpart is applicable.

§ 50.44 Restrictions on clinical investigations involving prisoners.

(a) Except as provided in § 50.44(b), clinical investigations regulated by the Food and Drug Administration under sections 505(i), 507(d), and 520(g) of the Federal Food, Drug, and Cosmetic Act, as well as clinical investigations that support applica-

tions for research or marketing permits for products regulated by the Food and Drug Administration may not involve prisoners as subjects.

(b) Clinical investigations that are regulated by the Food and Drug Administration under sections 505(i), 507(d), or 520(g) of the Federal Food, Drug, and Cosmetic Act, as well as clinical investigations that support applications for research or marketing permits for products regulated by the Food and Drug Administration, may involve prisoners as subjects only if the institution responsible for the conduct of the clinical investigation has certified to the Food and Drug Administration that the institutional review board has approved the clinical investigation under § 50.48; and

(1)(i) In the judgment of the Food and Drug Administration, the proposed clinical investigation involves solely research on practices both innovative and accepted, which have the intent and reasonable probability of improving, the health and well-being of the subjects;

(ii) In cases in which these studies require the assignment of prisoners in a manner consistent with protocols approved by the institutional review board to control groups that may not benefit from the research, the study may proceed only after the Food and Drug Administration has consulted with appropriate experts, including experts in penology, medicine, and ethics, and has published notice in the FEDERAL REGISTER of its intent to approve such research; or

(2) Research on conditions particularly affecting prisoners as a class (for example, vaccine trials and other research on hepatitis, which is much more prevalent in prisons than elsewhere) provided that the Food and Drug Administration has consulted with appropriate experts including experts in penology, medicine, and ethics, and has published notice in the FEDERAL REGISTER of its intent to approve such research; subject to the approval of the Federal Food

and Drug Administration, prisoners may participate in the research even though they are assigned, in a manner consistent with protocols approved by the institutional review board, to control groups that may not benefit from the research.

§ 50.46 Composition of institutional review boards where prisoners are involved.

In addition to satisfying any other requirements governing institutional review boards set forth in this chapter, an institutional review board, in carrying out responsibilities under this part with respect to research covered by this subpart, shall also meet the following specific requirements:

(a) A majority of the institutional review board (exclusive of prisoner members) shall have no association with the prison(s) involved, apart from their membership on the institutional review board.

(b) At least one member of the institutional review board shall be a prisoner, or a prisoner advocate with appropriate background and experience to serve in that capacity, except that if a particular research project is reveiwed by more than one institutional review board, only one institutional review board need satisfy this requirement.

§ 50.48 Additional duties of the institutional review boards where prisoners are involved.

(a) In addition to all other responsibilities prescribed for institutional review boards under this chapter, the institutional review board shall review clinical investigations covered by this subpart and approve such clinical investigations only if it finds that:

(1) The research under review represents one of the categories of research permitted under § 50.44(b) (1) and (2);

(2) Any possible advantages accruing to the prisoner through his or her participation in the clinical investigation, when compared to the general living conditions, medical care, quality of food, amenities, and oppor-

tunity for earnings in prison, are not of such a magnitude that his or her ability to weigh the risks of the clinical investigation against the value of such advantages in the limited-choice environment of the prison is impaired;

(3) The risks involved in the clinical investigation are commensurate with risks that would be accepted by nonprisoner volunteers;

(4) Procedures for the selection of subjects within the prison are fair to all prisoners and immune from arbitrary intervention by prison authorities or prisoners; unless the principal investigator provides to the institutional review board justification in writing for following some other procedures, control subjects must be selected randomly from the group of available prisoners who meet the characteristics needed for that research project;

(5) Any information given to the subjects is presented in language which is appropriate for the subject population;

(6) Adequate assurance exists that parole boards will not take into account a prisoner's participation in the clinical investigation in making decisions regarding parole, and each prisoner is clearly informed in advance that participation in the clinical investigation will have no effect on his or her parole; and

(7) Where the institutional review board finds there may be need for follow-up examination or care of participants after the end of their participation, adequate provision has been made for such examination or care, taking into account the varying lengths of individual prisoners' sentences, and for informing participants of this fact.

(b) The institutional review board shall carry out such other duties as may be assigned by the Food and Drug Administration.

(c) The institution shall certify to the Food and Drug Administration, in such form and manner as the Food and Drug Administration may require, that the duties of the institutional review board under this section have been fulfilled.

Appendix Two

Phase One Test Sites

The following list is a compilation of research sites where I have good reason to believe Phase One tests are being routinely conducted. As I said, this list probably only covers about a fifth of the existing sites around the world.

Canada

Medical Education Programs, Canada, Inc.
One West Pearce Street, Suite 305
Richmond Hills, Ontario L4B 3K3 Canada

England

Health and Sciences Research, Inc.
Surrey, England   011 44 372 464956

Alabama

Scientific Applications Company, Inc.
1714 11th Avenue South
Birmingham, AL 35205   205-933-2353

BioMed Research Clinical Research Center, Inc.
759 Valley Street
Birmingham, AL 35226   205-823-6180

Sorra, Inc.
1801 1st Avenue S #333
Birmingham, AL 35233-1935   205-250-8017

Birmingham Research Group, Inc.
PO Box 2850
Florence, AL 35630   205-863-3594

Drug Research & Analysis Corp.
PO Box 17447
Montgomery, AL 36117   205-265-2700

Arkansas

Clinical Investigation Specialists, Inc.
One Financial Centre,
650 Shackleford #235
Little Rock, AR 72211   501-227-0811

Arizona

Harris Laboratories Clinical
    Development Division
7432 East Stetson Drive
Scottsdale, AZ 85251   602-949-7089

Research Management, Inc.
8096 North 85th Way, Suite 105
Scottsdale, AZ 85258   602-951-9168

California

Inamed Development Co.
5421 Cameo Road
Carpenteria, CA 93013   805-684-3734

Bay Medical Research Foundation
118 E Tennessee Street
Fairfield, CA 94533   707-426-3179

Harbor/UCLA Medical Center
2408 Sylvan Lane
Glendale, CA 91208   213-533-3472

Institute for Biological Research & Development
2525 Campus Drive
Irvine, CA 92715   714-476-2727

Professional Research Network, Inc.
4330 Barranca Parkway, Suite 101-170
Irvine, CA 92714   714-733-0199

Freighner Research Institute
4400 Palm Avenue, Suite E
La Mesa, CA 92041   619-464-4564

The Phoenix
23441 South Pointe Drive, Suite 90
Laguna Hills, CA 92653   714-770-6866

Century Park Research Associates
2080 Century Park East, Suite 601
Los Angeles, CA 90067   213-553-0502

Crawforth Clinical Research Associates
PO Box 1421
Martinez, CA 94553   415-229-4865

Syntex (USA), Inc.
Research Division
3401 Hillview Avenue
PO Box 10850
Palo Alto, CA 94303   415-855-5202

Southwest Clinical Research
39-700 Bob Hope Drive, Suite 103
Rancho Mirage, CA 92270   619-773-9117

Clinical Research Advantage
115 South Palomar Drive
Redwood City, CA 94062   415-369-9888

Clinical Research Institute, Inc.
9855 Erma Road, Suite 133
San Diego, CA 92131   619-271-1690

Health and Sciences Research, Inc.
San Diego, CA   619-597-0788

International Clinical Research Corp.
5160 Carroll Canyon Road
San Diego, CA 92121   619-552-3400

Access Biotechnology, Inc.
395 Oyster Point Blvd., Suite 305
S. San Francisco, CA 94080   415-952-8400

Pharmaquest Corporation
3301 Kerner Blvd.
San Rafael, CA 94901   415-258-9510

Sunnyvale Medical Clinic, Inc.
596 Carroll Street
Sunnyvale, CA 94086   408-730-4242

San Diego Clinical Research Associates
550 West Vista Way, Suite 401
Vista, CA 92083   619-941-1261

Colorado

IND Clinical Research, Inc.
PO Box 440553
Aurora, CO 80044   303-750-8449

Boulder Clinical Research, Inc.
4891 Valkyrie
Boulder, CO 80301   303-530-7747

NDA Resources
790 Washington Street, Suite 301
Denver, CO 80203   303-832-3302

Pulmonary Drug Evaluation Program
3655 Lutheran Parkway, Suite 205
Wheat Ridge, CO 80033   303-467-9711

Connecticut

National Medical Research Corp.
25 Main Street
Hartford, CT 06106   203-724-0091

American Clinical Research Consultants
PO Box 7299
Wilton, CT 06897-7299   203-762-2097

District of Columbia

Clinical Research Consultants
2720 Chain Bridge Road NW
Washington, DC 20016   202-244-5550

Florida

Florida Clinical Research
700 West Hillsboro Blvd.,
   Bldg 3, Suite 107
Deerfield Beach, FL 33441   305-421-8312

Clinical Physiology Associates
4110 Center Point Drive,
   Suite 219
Metro Park Plaza
Fort Myers, FL 33916   813-936-4421

Southeastern Clinical Research Consultants
PO Box 521743
Longwood, FL 32752-1743   407-332-7975

Pan American Pharmacological
701 NW 57th Avenue, Suite 220
Miami, FL 33126   305-261-7761

Quality Research Group
1680 Michigan Avenue, Suite 900
Miami Beach, FL 33139   305-532-4470

South Florida Bioavailability Clinic, Inc.
530 Biscayne Blvd.
Miami, FL 33132   305-381-8610

Medical Education & Research Corp.
8333 North Davis Highway
Pensacola, FL 32514   904-474-8427

Concepts in Pharmaceutical Research
457 Fellsmere Road, Suite D
Sebastian, FL 32958   407-388-0721

Criterium Clinical Research Services
606 King Louis Ct
Seffner, FL 33584   813-689-7705

Clinical Research Coordinators, Inc.
400 West Morse Blvd., Suite 102
Winter Park, FL 32789   407-740-8667

Georgia

Biobehavioral Research Center
2784 North Decatur Road, Suite 130
Atlanta, GA 30033   404-292-2000

Medical Parameters, Inc.
534 Wessex Drive
Evans, GA 30809   404-855-7405

D. Blum & Associates
5082 Laurel Bridge Drive
Smyrna, GA 30082   404-458-1276

Iowa

U.S. Medical Research
MUI Box 1028
Fairfield, IA 52556   515-472-1129

Illinois

University Hospital Consortium
One Mid America Plaza, Suite 700
Oakbrook Terrace, IL 60181   708-954-4707

University Hospital Consortium
2001 Spring Road, Suite 700
Oak Brook, IL 60521-1890   708-954-1700

Praire Education & Research
   Cooperative
PO Box 19420
Springfield, IL 62794-9420   217-788-0706

Premier Hospitals Alliance, Inc.
Three Westbrook Corporate Center
9th Floor
Westchester, IL 60154   708-409-3752

Indiana

Clinical Research Consulting, Inc.
11051 Kahre Court
Evansville, IN 47710   812-867-6508

GFI Phamaceutical Services, Inc.
401 Southeast Sixth Street
Evansville, IN 47713   812-422-3531

Lilly Laboratory for Clinical Research
Wishard Memorial Hospital
1001 West 10th St
Indianapolis, IN 46202   317-276-4948

SciCor, Inc.
8200 SciCor Drive
Indianapolis, IN 46234   317-271-1200

Heartland Research Center
100 East Wayne Street #545
South Bend, IN 46601   219-287-9626

BAS Analytics
1205 Kent Avenue
W Lafayette, IN 47906   317-463-4527

Kansas
Pharmaceutical Consultants, Inc.
11229 Nall, Suite 100
Leawood, KS 66211   800-331-7114

Clinical Reference Laboratory
11850 West 85th Street
Lenexa, KS 66214   913-492-3652

Louisiana
Margo Morgan Research Center, Inc.
3622 Bienville Street
New Orleans, LA 70119   504-484-6664

Massachusetts
Clinical Data, Inc.
(Drug Research Services Division)
1172 Commonwealth Avenue
Boston, MA 02134   617-734-3700

Medical and Technical Research Associates, Inc.
320 Washington Street
Boston, MA 02135   617-782-6872

Parexel International Corp.
One Alewife Place
Cambridge, MA 02140   617-491-7330

Evaluations, Inc.
Eighty Bridge Street
Dedham, MA 02026   617-326-6699

Clinical Research Associates, Inc.
634 Washington Street
Holliston, MA 01746   508-429-2657

Pharmaceutical Development Associates of New England
82 Furnace Street
Marshfield, MA 02050   617-834-1930

Medical & Technical Research Associates, Inc.
32 Kearney Road
Needham, MA 02194   617-444-2922

Maryland

ANTECH, Inc.
Hopkins/Bayview Research Campus
PO Box 5261
Baltimore, MD 21224   301-550-2922

Clinical Science Research International
Signet Tower
7 Paul Street, Suite 1650
Baltimore, MD 21202   301-962-5371

Charles S. Dawson Associates, Inc.
29 Parliament Court
Baltimore, MD 21212   301-377-4505

PharaKinetics Laboratories, Inc.
302 West Fayette St
Baltimore, MD 21201   301-385-4500

Clinical Sciences, Inc.
4405 East-West Highway
Bethesda, MD 20814   301-652-1161

Program Resources, Inc.
(Biolog Response Modifiers Program)
501 West 7th Street #3
Frederick, MD 21701   301-846-1520

Powers & Associates
3107 Jackson Ridge Court
Phoenix, MD 21131-1461   301-785-0045

International Drug Registration, Inc.
14915 Broschart Rd
Rockville, MD 20850   301-294-1900

Medifacts Ltd.
11900 Parklawn Drive #120
Rockville, MD 20852   301-230-1304

International Clinical Services, Inc.
15500 Gallaudet Avenue
Silver Springs, MD 20905   301-384-1554

Maine

Clinical Research Management, Inc.
158 Veranda Street
PO Box 1437
Portland, ME 04104   207-774-3980

Michigan

Drug Research, P.C.
901 Mt. Hope, 1st Floor
Lansing, MI 48910   517-482-2912

Minnesota

Minnesota Clinical Study Center
7505 University Avenue NE
Minneapolis, MN 55432   612-571-4200

Missouri

Gateway Medical Research , Inc.
142 North Main Street
Charles, MO 63301   314-947-4209

Berger-Boyer & Associates, Inc.
3614 Main Street
Kansas City, MO 64111   816-561-0603

International Medical Technical Consultants, Inc.
31 East 68th Terrace
Kansas City, MO 64113   913-599-4100

Quincy Research Center
5104 East 24th Street
Kansas City, MO 64127   816-483-1850

Biomedical Systems
1034 South Brentwood Blvd. #860
St. Louis, MO 63117   314-727-7098

Family Medicine of Saint Louis
St. Louis, MO   314-768-3204

Nebraska

Harris Laboratories, Inc.
624 Peach Street
Box 80837
Lincoln, NE 68501   402-476-2811

New Jersey

Phoenix International Life Sciences
98 Autumn Ridge Road
Bedminster, NJ 07921   215-321-0033

The Hardardt Group
PO Box 867
Bernardsville, NJ 07924   201-425-3930

ClinCon Research, Inc.
535 Main Street
Chester, NJ 07930   201-879-8826

Oxford Research International Corp.
1425 Broad Street
Clifton, NJ 07013-4221   201-777-2800

Riverview Clinical Studies Center
Meridian Center III
6 Industrial Way West
Eatontown, NJ 07724   201-389-0529

UBG International, Inc.
Meridian Center III
6B Industrial Way West
Eatontown, NJ 07724

Health and Sciences Research, Inc.
401 South Van Brunt Street
Englewood, NJ 07631   800-223-4968/201-567-8380

Biotrax Research, Inc.
22-08 Route 208 South
Fair Lawn, NJ 07410   201-794-6300

Clinical Protocol Associates, Inc.
One Bridge Plaza North, Suite 120
Fort Lee, NJ 07024   201-947-2774

Cardio Data Systems Research
56 Haddon Avenue, Box 200
Haddon Field, NJ 08033   609-354-2222

HLS Clinical Systems
150 Clove Road, PO Box 422
Little Falls, NJ 07424   201-785-8500

TKL Research, Inc.
255 West Spring Valley Avenue
Maywood, NJ 07607   201-587-0500

The Phoenix Clinical Research Management Company
Mt. Arlington Corporate Center
200 Valley Road #205
Mt. Arlington, NJ 07856   201-770-1800

G.H. Besselaar Associates
103 College Road East
Princeton, NJ 08540   609-452-8550

In Vivo, Inc.
214 Carnegie Center
Princeton, NJ 08543   609-520-0024

Advanced Clinical & Epidemiological Research, Inc.
31 Mayflower Drive
Red Bank, NJ 07701   908-964-0858

LAB, Inc.
700 Grand Avenue
Ridgefield, NJ 07657   201-943-1180

M. Hurley and Associates, Inc.
1 Springfield Avenue
Summit, NJ 07901   201-522-9119

Future Healthcare Research, Inc.
101 Old Short Hills Road
W. Orange, NJ 07052   201-731-7484

New York

Clinical Technologies Associates, Inc.
5 Westchester Plaza
Elmsford, NY 10523   914-347-2220

Research Testing Laboratories, Inc.
255 Great Neck Road
Great Neck, NY 11021   516-773-7788

Clinical Drug Investigators, Inc.
333 Broadway, Suite 2000
Jericho, NY 11753   516-822-4445

Barton & Polanski Associates, Inc.
845 Third Avenue, 21st Floor
New York, NY 10022   212-688-4343

Pharmaceutical Research Network, Inc.
111-05 Jamaica Avenue
Richmond Hill, NY 11418   718-441-3415

Oneida Research Services, Inc.
One Halsey Rd
Whitesboro, NY 13492   315-736-3050

North Carolina

Cato Research, Ltd.
4364 South Alston Avenue, Suite 201
Durham, NC 27713

Carolina Research Group
PO Box 32295
Raleigh, NC 27622   919-881-9900

Clinical Research International, Inc.
PO Box 13991
Research Triangle Park, NC 27709   919-544-3900

Family Health International
PO Box 13950
Research Triangle Park, NC 27705   919-544-7040

Research Triangle Institute
PO Box 12194
Research Triangle Park, NC 27709   919-541-7280

Quintiles, Inc.
PO Box 13979
Research Triangle Park, NC 27709-3979   919-941-2888

Pharmaceutical Product Development, Inc.
202 North 3rd Street, 4th Floor
Wilmington, NC 28401   919-251-0081

Piedmont Research Associates, Inc.
1901 South Hawthorne Road, Suite 310
Winston-Salem, NC 27103   919-768-8062

North Dakota

PRACS Institute
2601 North University Drive
Fargo, ND 58102   701-239-4750

Ohio

Akron Internists Research Foundation, Inc.
75 Arch Street, Suite 302
Akron, OH 44304   216-375-3314

Clinical Studies, Inc.
635 Forty Sixth Street NW
Canton, OH 44709   216-493-8822

Cardiovascular Research Center at Christ Hospital
2139 Auburn Avenue
Cincinnati, OH 45219   513-721-4278

Center for Research in Sleep Disorders
1275 Kemper Road
Cincinnati, OH 45246   513-671-3101

Hilltop Pharmatest, Inc.
3333 Vine Street, Suite 101
Cincinnati, OH 45220   513-281-2989

Kindle Research Associates
105 West 4th Street Suite 610
Cincinnati, OH 45202   513-381-5550

Kreindler Medical Associates
Research Department
7743 Five Mile Road
Cincinnati, OH 45230   513-232-9191

Oregon

Clinical Trials Systems, Inc.
305 Northeast 102nd Avenue
Portland, OR 97220   503-256-3056

NorthWest Research Associates, Inc.
4001 Northeast Halsey, Suite 3
Portland, OR 97232   503-287-3533

Pennsylvania

Bio-Pharm Clinical Services, Inc.
4 Valley Square,
512 Township Line Road
Blue Bell, PA 19422   215-283-0770

Barnett International
415 East 22nd Street
Chester, PA 19013   215-876-5500

Argus Research Laboratories, Inc.
905 Sheehy Driver
Horsham, PA 19044   215-443-8710

New Drug Services, Inc.
415 McFarlan Road, Suite 201
Kennett Square, PA 19348   215-444-4722

Biodecision Clinical Research Institute
5001 Baum Blvd.
Pittsburgh, PA 19422   412-682-5582

Med-Check Laboratories, Inc.
4900 Perry Highway
Pittsburgh, PA 15229   412-931-7200

PACT
150 Radnor-Chester Road, Suite D200
St. Davids, PA 19087   215-687-5454

Tennessee

Clinical Trial Management Services
PO Box 1085
Bristol, TN 37621-1085   615-968-9533

CTMS, Inc.
501 Fifth Street
Bristol, TN 37620   615-968-9533

Horizons Research
PO Box 808
Johnson City, TN 37605   615-929-0073

Intermountain Clinical Research Associates, Inc.
109 Ford Avenue
Kingsport, TN 37663   801-255-1079

Health First Medical Group
850 Ridgelake Blvd., Suite GO2
Memphis, TN 38119   901-762-5730

ClinTrials, Inc.
3401 West End Avenue, Suite 310
Nashville, TN 37203   615-386-3213

Texas

HealthQuest Research
3807 Spicewood Springs Road, Suite 200
Austin, TX 78759   512-345-7776

Pharmaco Dynamics Research, Inc.
Two Park Plaza, 4009 Bannister Lane
Austin, TX 78704   512-447-2663

G & S Studies, Inc.
4245 Wellborn Road
Bryan, TX 77801   409-846-5933

TEAMS - Technical Evaluation & Management Systems
1110 Presonwood Towers
5151 Beltline Road
Dallas, TX 75240   214-386-4900

Nu-Med Clinical Research, Inc.
1100 N Stanton, Suite 410
El Paso, TX 79902   915-833-7944

Med-Tech Research, Inc.
8830 Long Point #601
Houston, TX 77055   713-467-0609

reSearch for Health, Inc.
902 Frostwood #315
Houston, TX 77024   713-932-1234

Facilitators of Applied Clinical Trials (FACT)
85 Northeast Loop 410, Suite 612
San Antonio, TX 78216   512-377-3725

Sylvana Research
7711 Louis Pasteur, Suite 406
San Antonio, TX 78229   512-558-3131

Utah

Jean Brown Associates, Inc.
PO Box 510604
Salt Lake City, UT 84151-0604   801-359-3351

Virginia

Biometric Research Institute, Inc.
1401 Wilson Blvd., Suite 400
Arlington, VA 22209-2306   703-276-0400

Pharmaceutical Research Associates
1290 Seminole Trail
Charlottesville, VA 22901-1736   804-978-7730

Education & Research Foundation
2602 Langhorne Road
Lynchburg, VA 24501   804-847-5695

Whitby Research, Inc.
2801 Reserve Street
PO Box 27426
Richmond, VA 23261-7426   804-254-4026

Washington

Puget Sound Medical Investigators
140 North Percival Street
Olympia, WA 98502   206-357-6689

Pacific Biometrics, Inc.
1100 Eastlake Avenue East
Seattle, WA 98109   206-233-9602/233-9151

Coordinators of Clinical Research
505 West Riverside, Suite 500
Spokane, WA 99201   509-458-0444

Wisconsin

Hazelton Wisconsin, Inc.
3301 Kinsman Blvd.
Madison, WI 53704   608-242-2629

Quant Data
PO Box 23651
Milwaukee, WI 53223   414-963-8540

West Virginia

Clinical & Pharmacologic Research, Inc.
1052 Maple Drive
Morgantown, WV 26505   304-599-1197

Appendix Three

Sample Organ Donation Form

Consent for Organ and Tissue Donation

Out of consideration for those in need, and by reason of my relationship to the deceased, I hereby consent to the removal of the following organs or tissue for transplantation or the advancement of medical science and education.

I,_____, authorize the donation of the following
      (full legal name of next of kin)

organs/tissue from _____.
                  (full legal name of donor)

Tissues

_____ Eyes

_____ Bone and connective tissue

_____ Skin grafts

_____ Heart for valves

_____ Additional research tissues

Limitations: _____

Organs

_____ Kidneys

_____ Heart

_____ Lungs

_____ Liver

_____ Pancreas

_____ Other (specify)

I understand that tissue samples may be tested and pertinent diagnostic and medical information will be reviewed to assure medical suitability and that all donors must be tested for transmissible diseases (AIDS, hepatitis, syphilis) before transplantation can occur.

I hereby acknowledge that this consent is voluntarily given and motivated by humanitarian instincts without expectation of reward or compensation. It implies no obligation on the part of the recipient, this facility or its designees. Distribution and determination of use of these gifts will be coordinated by the procurement program in accordance with medical and ethical standards.

I understand that any additional charges directly associated with the donation will be covered by the procurement agency. Disposition of the body after the removal and tissue will remain the responsibility of the next of kin.

_____

Signature of next of kin   Date/time   Relationship

_____

Address   Phone

_____

City/State/Zip

_____

Signature of person obtaining consent   Date

_____

Witness   Date

_____

Facility   City/State

Appendix Four

Organ/Tissue Banks

The following organizations may be of help in locating both organs and those who are looking for organs.

LifeBanc
1909 East 101st Street
Cleveland, OH 44106   216-791-5433

These guys run programs to promote the transplantation of all types of organs and tissues, run a 24-hour "recovery team" and train hospital staff in organ recovery.

American Liver Foundation
1425 Pompton Avenue
Cedar Grove, NJ 07009   201-256-2550/800-223-0179

As the name implies, this outfit concerns itself with livers — not only their transplantation but the different diseases that affect them. They run awareness programs to promote donation.

Children's Liver Foundation
14245 Ventura Blvd., Suite 201
Sherman Oaks, CA 91423   818-906-3021/800-526-1593

These guys push hard for more liver transplants, especially for children. A lot of the members are parents or friends of kids with liver problems.

American Society of Transplant Surgeons
716 Lee Street
Des Plaines, IL 60016   708-824-5700

This is a group of transplant surgeons who offer their expertise to educate the public about transplant surgery and to help out recipients of organ transplants.

American Transplant Association
PO Box 822123
Dallas, TX 75382-2123   214-340-0942

They run an international transplant "network" that tries to provide financial and other help to families of organ recipients. They also try to run programs designed to increase public awareness of transplant surgery.

Pittsburgh Transplant Foundation
5743 Center Avenue
Pittsburgh, PA 15206   412-366-6777/800-366-6777

Specializing in organ removal, this foundation also has access to UNOS (a national computer matching system for organs and tissues).

United Network for Organ Sharing (UNOS)
1100 Boulders Pkwy., Suite 500
PO Box 13770
Richmond, VA 23225   804-330-8500/800-24-DONOR

This is an enormous clearinghouse for organs and tissues, transplant centers, and tissue-typing labs. Its Organ Center matches patients with donated organs and sets up transportation of organs to transplant sites. Set up by law as a national center for all organs, this is the best place to look for an organ you need, or to find someone who needs your organs, as UNOS has access to all organ registries for both donors and recipients.

Appendix Five

Sample Page from a
Sperm Bank's Donor Catalog

DONOR CATALOG

This catalog contains all donors in the Caucasians program. Please check with the lab for specimen availability.

CAUCASIANS

Donor ID	Heritage	Blood Type	Hair Color/Type	Eye Color	Skin	HT	WT	Yrs Ed/ College	Occupation Skills & Interests	No. In Stock
F 1091	Cauc/Ita/Dut/Iri	A+	Brown/straight	Brown	Fair	5-5	125	2	Student/communicatio electronic music/pho	40
F 1092	Cauc/Wel/Iri/Eng	A+	Brown/straight	Blue	Fair	6-2	240	3	Student/microbiology camping/reading/outd	105
F 1100	Cauc/Eng	O+	Brown/Straight	Blue	Fair	6-0	185	1	Student/engineering outdoors/fishing	1
F 1103	Cauc/Eng/Iri	A+	Brown/straight	Blue	Fair	6-2	195	5	Accountant	
F 1105	Cauc/Ger/Iri/Pol	A+	Brown/straight	Brown	Medium	6-1	193	2	Student/computers weight lifting/art	17
F 1107	Cauc/Iri/Ger/Eng	A+	Black/straight	Blue	Fair	5-10	170	3	Student/education tennis/riding horses	
F 1108	Cauc/Ger/Swe	O+	Blond/straight	Blue	Fair	6-0	175	7	Medical student sports/reading	
F 1115	Cauc/Ger/Fre	O+	Brown/straight	Brown	Medium	5-8	150		Control board oper sports/guns	2
F 1117	Cauc/Eng/Ger	O+	Blond/straight	Blue	Fair	5-7	145	4	Student/chemical eng computers/model buil	5
F 1127	Cauc/Iri	B+	Blond/straight	Brown	Fair	5-8	145	4	Restaurant manager bicycling/fitness	106
F 1132	Cauc/Ger	O+	Blond/straight	Blue	Fair	5-10	150		Vending route driver Race car driver/sport	54
F 1139	Cauc/Ger	O-	Blond/straight	Blue	Fair	5-9	152	7	Exec dir govt agency	173
F 1144	Cauc/Iri/Ita/ Eng	A-	Brown/straight	Brown	Medium	5-10	199	3	Student/pre-med read/music/wt lifting	
F 1148	Cauc/Eng/Sco/ Ger	A+	Brown/straight	Blue	Fair	6-2	210	4	Corp consultant	

Appendix Six

Sperm Banks in the
United States and Canada

Ann Arbor Reproductive Medicine Association
4990 Clark Road, Suite 100
Ypsilanti, MI 48197   313-434-4766
Director: E.P. Peterson, M.D.

Arizona Fertility Institute
2850 North 24th Street, Suite 500
Phoenix, AZ 85008   602-468-3840
Director: Robert H. Tamis, M.D.

Astarte Lab, Inc.
Jacksonville Hospital
PO Box 0070
Jacksonville, AL 36265   205-435-3953
Director: Carol S. Armon, **M.D.**   205-435-1122

Biogenetics Corporation
1330 Route 22 West
PO Box 1290
Mountainside, NJ 07092   1-800-942-4646
Director: Albert Anouna

California Cryobank, Inc.
1019 Gayley Avenue
Los Angeles, CA 90024   213-553-9828
Co-Directors: Charles Sims, M.D.   800-223-3588
C.M. Rothman, M.D.

Center for Reproduction and Transplantation Immunology
Methodist Hospital of Indiana
1701 North Senate Blvd.
Indianpolis, IN 46202   317-929-6158
Director: John K. Critser, Ph.D.

Cleveland Clinic Sperm Bank
Cleveland Clinic Foundation
A-1-191
9500 Euclid Avenue
Cleveland, OH 44106   216-444-2488
Director: Susan Rothmann, Ph.D.

Cryo Laboratory Facility
100 East Ohio Suite 268
Chicago, IL 60601   312-751-2632
Director: Alfred Morris

Cryobiology
4830-D Knightsbridge Blvd.
Columbus, OH 43214   614-451-4375
Director: William Baird, Ph.D.

Cryogenic Laboratories, Inc.
2233 Hamline Avenue North
Roseville, MN 55113   612-636-3792
Director: John H. Olson, M.S.

Evanston/Glenbrook Hospital
Department of Obstetrics and Gynecology
2050 Pfingsten Road, Suite 350
Glenview, IL 60025   708-657-5700
Director: Marybeth Gerrity, Ph.D.

Fairfax Cryobank
A Division of the Genetics and IVF Institute
3015 Williams Drive, Suite 110
Fairfax, VA 22031   703-698-3976
Director: Edward Fugger, Ph.D.

Fertility Institute of New Orleans
6020 Bullard Avenue
New Orleans, LA 70128   504-246-8971
Director: Terry Olar, Ph.D.

Fertility Institute of Southern California
1125 East 17th Street, W-120
Santa Ana, CA 92701   714-953-5683
Director: Linda Sullivan

Genetic Semen Bank
University of Nebraska Medical Center
42nd and Dewey Avenue
Omaha, NE 68105   402-559-5070
Director: Warren Sanger, Ph.D.

Grant Hospital of Chicago
Chicago IVF and Fertility Institute
550 Webster Avenue
Chicago, IL 60614   312-883-3866
Director: W. Paul Dmowski, M.D.

Hoxworth Blood Center
University of Cincinnati Medical Center
3231 Burnett Avenue, M.L. #55
Cincinnati, OH 45267   513-569-1123
Director: Charles Mayhaus

Idant Laboratory
645 Madison
New York, NY 10022   212-935-1430
Director: Joseph Feldschuh, M.D.

International Cryogenics, Inc.
189 Townsend, Suite 203
Birmingham, MI 48009   313-644-5822
Director: Mary Ann Brown

Jefferson Semen Bank
Department of Urology
Jefferson Medical College
1025 Walnut Street
Philadelphia, PA 19107   215-955-6961
Director: Irvin Hirsch, M.D.

Midwest Fertility Foundation and Laboratory
3101 Broadway, Suite 650-A
Kansas City, MO 64111   816-756-0040
Director: Elwyn Grimes, M.D.

New England Sperm Bank (Newton Laboratory)
Pratt Building
2014 Washington Street
Newton, MA 02162   617-332-1228
Co-Directors: Robert A. Newton, M.D.
Betty Hargis, Ph.D.

Northern California Cryobank
5821 Jameson Ct.
Carmichael, CA 95608   916-486-0451
Director: Marvin Kamras, M.D.

Paces Cryobank and Infertility Services
3193 Howell Mill Road, Suite 322
Atlanta, GA 30327   404-350-5561
Director: Diana Snoey

Regional Andrology Facility
University of Ottawa
501 Smyth Road
Ottawa, Ontario, Canada K1H 86   613-737-8559
Director: Arthur Leader, M.D.

The Repository of Germinal Choice
PO Box 2876
Escondido, CA 92025   619-743-0772
Director: Robert Graham

Reproductive Genetics Group
Swedish Hospital
747 Summit Avenue
Seattle, WA 98104   206-386-2483
Director: Lawrence Karp, M.D.

Reproductive Resources
4740 I-10 Service Road, Suite 340
Metairie, LA 70001   504-454-7973/
Director: Brenda Bordson, Ph.D.   800-227-4561

Reproductive Lab
336 East 30th Street
New York, NY 10016   212-779-3988
Director: Philippe Bailly, M.S.

Rochester Regional Cryobank
Andrology Laboratory
Box 668
Department of Obstetrics and Gynecology
University of Rochester
601 Elmwood Avenue
Rochester, NY 14642   716-275-3084
Director: Grace Centola, Ph.D.

Rocky Mountain Cryobank
PO Box 2156
Jackson, WY 83001   307-733-9170
Director: William Racow

Southwest Fertility Center
3125 North 32nd Street
Phoenix, AZ 85108   602-956-7481
Director: Sujatha Gunnala, Ph.D.

Drs. Sparr, Stephens and Associates
8160 Walnut Hill Lane, Suite 324
Dallas, TX 75231   214-691-0924
Director: Stacy Stephens, M.D.

Sperm Bank of California
3007 Telegraph Avenue, Suite 2
Oakland, CA 94609   415-444-2014
Director: Barbara Raboy

Tyler Medical Clinic
921 Westwood Blvd.
Los Angeles, CA 90024   213-272-1905
Director: Stanley Friedman, M.D.   213-272-5573

University of Arkansas for Medical Sciences
Semen Cryobank — Slot 708
4301 West Markham Street
Little Rock, AR 72205   501-686-8450
Director: J.K. Sherman, Ph.D. (Dr. Sherman is also Chairman of AATB Reproductive Council)

University McDonald Women's Hospital
2074 Abington Road
Cleveland, OH 44106   212-844-3317
Director: Leon Sheean, Ph.D.

University of Missouri-Columbia School of Medicine
Department of Urology
Health Sciences Center N510
One Hospital Drive
Columbia, MO 65212   314-882-7176
Director: Jawad Ali, Ph.D.

University of Texas Southwestern Medical Center
Andrology and Reproductive Endocrinology Laboratory
Department of Obstetrics and Gynecology
Dallas, TX 75235   214-688-2376
Director: William Byrd, Ph.D.

University of Wisconsin Clinical Sciences Center
Department of Obstetrics and Gynecology
600 Highland Avenue
Madison, WI 53705   608-263-1217
Director: Sander Shapiro, M.D.

Washington Fertility Study Center
2600 Virginia Avenue North West #500
Washington, DC 20037   202-333-3100
Director: Sal Leto, Ph.D.

Western Cryobank
2010 East Bijou
Colorado Springs, CO 80909   719-578-9014
Director: Charles Johnson, D.O.

Xytex Corporation
1100 Emmett Street
Augusta, GA 30904   1-800-277-3210
Director: Armand Karow, Ph.D.

Zygen Laboratory
16742 Stagg Street, Unit 105
Van Nuys, CA 91406   818-988-2500
Director: Cyrus Milani, M.D.

YOU WILL ALSO WANT TO READ: